DUCK

DUCKS

David Tomlinson

WITH ILLUSTRATIONS BY NICHOLAS PIKE

Whittet Books

TITLE PAGE ILLUSTRATION: *Long-tailed ducks*

First published 1996
Text ©1996 by David Tomlinson
Illustrations ©1996 by Nicholas Pike
Whittet Books Ltd, 18 Anley Road, London W14 OBY

Cataloguing in publication data
A catalogue record for this book is available from the British Library.

ISBN 1 873580 24 X

Printed and bound by Biddles of Guildford

Contents

Introduction

My enthusiasm for ducks was kindled before I could walk: my mother used to take me in the pushchair to the local park to feed the ducks. It was only in later years I discovered that full-winged exotic wildfowl from a nearby collection used to flight into this park, so I was probably feeding mandarins and Carolina wood ducks as well as mallard. It seems likely that I was imprinted on wildfowl at an impressionable age. I was eight years old when I first visited the Wildfowl Trust at Slimbridge, and I can still remember the excitement at seeing all those exotic ducks for the first time.

This passion for birds with webbed feet stayed with me, and in my teens I kept a small collection of ornamental wildfowl on the pond in my parents' garden. I was then able to lie in bed at night and listen to my wigeon whistle, or to study the display of my drake mandarin. I started to write about ducks while still at school, and the first article I ever had published, in *Cage and Aviary Birds*, was a comparison of mandarins and Carolinas.

My travels in the last twenty years have allowed me to see the majority of the world's ducks in the wild. I have many vivid memories of watching ducks in far-away places: ruddy shelduck on the steppes of Kirghizstan; king eiders on Herschel Island in the Canadian Arctic; steamer ducks in the Falklands; white-cheeked pintail and Andean ruddy ducks on a Patagonian lake high in the Andes; red shoveler on the Pampas; muscovies on the Madrigal estuary in Costa Rica; pygmy geese in Botswana's Okavango delta; radjah shelduck in Australia's Kakadu National Park; harlequin ducks in Iceland ... However, you don't have to travel far to enjoy duck-watching. Regular visits to your local reservoir, gravel pit or park are bound to produce some exciting and unexpected observations, and even the familiar mallard is an entertaining bird to study.

In *Ducks* I have tried to get over some of my enthusiasm for the subject, as well as including those facts and figures that duck-watchers might like to know. Anyone with a serious interest in ducks (and wildfowl and water birds) should join the Wildfowl and Wetlands Trust, Slimbridge, Gloucestershire GL2 7BT. I have been a member for many years, and remain a regular visitor to the Trust's various centres.

David Tomlinson

A diversity of drakes: (clockwise from top right) *king eider, pink-eared duck, musk duck, hooded merganser, cotton pygmy goose, harlequin duck, common goldeneye, common shelduck, Australasian shoveler*

What is a duck?

If you had to describe a duck in ten words, what would you say? 'A rounded waterbird, with large beak, webbed feet. Quacks noisily.' Most people would probably be able to identify a duck from that description, but the authoritative *Dictionary of Birds* puts it differently. 'The substantive name of most of the smaller species of Anatidae.' That's the more technical definition, but it doesn't really help (and it is 11 words). Read on and you discover that the word duck does not correspond with the taxonomic subdivisions of the Anatidae, or, in other words, you can call a goose a duck, or a duck a goose, and it doesn't really matter. The Australian maned goose is not a goose at all, but a duck, while all three species of pygmy geese are really ducks, too. The knob-billed duck is a big hefty brute that could pass for a goose, which explains why it is sometimes called a knob-billed goose. It is, however, a duck.

The family Anatidae includes all the ducks, geese and swans, all of which are closely related to one another. Just to prove the point, domestic ducks (descended from mallard) have been known to hybridise with domestic geese (descended from greylags). Whether you call the resulting offspring deese or gucks is a moot point.

Experts differ on just how many species of Anatidae they recognise, and the current count is anything from 147 to 160. These figures include the geese and swans, but for convenience we are going to ignore them here, and concentrate just on ducks. This does produce one difficulty with the so-called sheldgeese from South America, which have closer affinities with the shelducks than the geese. However, we have to draw the line somewhere, so the poor old sheldgeese are going to be ignored. (They are a very quarrelsome bunch, so they won't like this too much.) A good case could be argued for leaving out the tropical whistling ducks, too, as in many ways they are more closely related to the swans and geese than the ducks. But as they happen to be one of my favourite groups, so they are going to be included.

With the geese, swans and sheldgeese excluded, we are left with a mere 120 or so species of ducks. Their taxonomy has been much debated, and no two authorities seem to agree. However, many of the time-honoured classifications have now been dropped, and many of the old groupings have been abandoned. In the appendix I include a list of all the ducks of the world in the latest (though still controversial) order.

As we will soon discover, my ten-word description of a duck only describes a minority of the 120 species. Some ducks have small beaks, not all are well rounded, and only a minority quack. However, they all have webbed feet, and everyone can swim without the aid of a rubber ring. Some spend a lot of time swimming, a few do virtually nothing else, while some prefer to paddle. Most of them are accomplished fliers, capable of covering huge

common shelduck

white-faced
whistling duck

mallard

eider

Carolina wood duck

red-breasted merganser (above)
goldeneye (below)

tufted duck

ruddy duck

Typical representatives of the eight main duck groupings

distances in migration; others have lost the power of flight entirely. And contrary to popular belief, only a minority eat fish. Most are vegetarian, but some are insectivorous, while many are omnivorous. All in all, ducks are a pretty diverse and adaptable bunch of birds, which explains why there are few parts of the globe (apart from Antarctica) where they are absent.

White-faced whistling ducks

Duck families
from whistlers to wigeon

Whistling ducks

Long-legged, long-necked and short-bodied, whistling ducks are distinctively different in appearance and behaviour, from all the other ducks. There are eight members of the whistling duck family, all of which are found (more or less) in the Tropics. All eight whistlers share a number of characteristics. Both the male and the female look alike, with no sexual or seasonal variation. Like most geese and swans, they stay paired together for life. (However, detailed studies would be sure to show plenty of cases of divorce and infidelity.) One spin-off of staying together is that both sexes share the incubation of the eggs, and help rear the young – they make excellent parents in captivity. In flight they all look alike – hump-backed and broad-winged – and flap their wings relatively slowly, though with relatively shallow beats. Unlike almost all the other ducks, they do not fly in formation, but in loose, noisy flocks. As their name suggests, they are great whistlers, especially when flying. The whistling no doubt helps the pairs (and perhaps their offspring) to keep in contact with each other.

Stifftails

The best-known member of the stifftail group (which comprises nine species) is the aptly named **ruddy duck**, as in Britain this charming and entertaining stifftail is proving to be a ruddy nuisance, due to its tendency to wander off to Spain and seduce **white-headed ducks**. (See the chapter on Aliens, p. 85). Now well established in Britain, the ruddy duck is really a North American bird, and the only member of the stifftail family with an extensive range in the northern hemisphere. The majority of the stifftails are birds of the tropics, or of the warm, sub-tropical zones. All favour fresh or brackish water, though the ruddy duck not infrequently occurs on coastal waters in North America. All the main members of the family, with two notable exceptions, look alike, but as their ranges rarely overlap in the wild, telling them apart is not usually difficult. It is the range separation that has allowed so many species to evolve, for the arrival of the alien ruddy duck in Spain shows how readily members of the family will hybridise. Stifftail is a good description of the family, for with one exception they all have long, stiff, tail feathers. When resting, the tail usually sticks up from the water at an angle of 45°, but when diving or swimming, it is laid flat on the water surface.

Shelduck

Bold, aggressive, noisy – all three are adjectives which can be applied to members of the Tadorninae, which includes the shelducks and the sheldgeese. Because this is a book on ducks, not geese, we are going to ignore the latter, which means omitting the Egyptian goose, now naturalised in England, and

Drake musk duck

the group of South American sheldgeese. The shelducks are all big birds, and though the males and females may share similar plumage, the former is invariably bigger and heavier than his mate. None of the shelducks have an eclipse plumage (see p. 72), but the majority do undergo moult migrations, often joining together on the moulting grounds in flocks of hundreds or even thousands of birds. Like the whistling ducks, but unlike almost every duck, they form lasting pair bonds, and with most species pairs stay together for life. Though all the shelducks are widely kept in captivity, they tend to bully (or even kill) smaller ducks, particularly during the breeding season. This limits their appeal in mixed collections. The Australian and paradise shelducks tend to be the most dangerous of the lot, and also the noisiest.

Steamers

Steamer ducks are the heavyweights of the duck world: big and aggressive, they are restricted to the southern tip of South America and the Falkland Islands. They are the southern counterparts of the northern eiders, filling a similar ecological niche by living on the coast and feeding on a diet of mussels and crustaceans. They are, however, much larger than the eiders. A big

Radjah shelduck

drake **Magellanic steamer** might weigh as much as 6.5 kilos (14lb), though an average weight is around 4.5 kilos (10lb). In the past their size has been much exaggerated; Captain Cook, one of the first Europeans to get to know this species, reported weights of between 13 and 13.5 kilos (29 and 30lb). Even so, a 6 kilo (14lb) duck is an impressive bird.

Steamers are coastal birds, seldom found far out to sea. They feed by upending or diving – when they dive, they use their stubby wings for assistance. Their large feet allow them to swim at considerable speed, and a maximum of 15 knots has been recorded. Their name comes from the fact that when swimming at speed, they resemble old-fashioned paddle-steamers splashing through the water. Because of their aggressive natures, they are rare in captivity, and cannot be mixed with other birds.

Taxonomists recognise four different species, three of which are flightless. As you might expect, it is the **flying steamer duck** that is the most widespread, as it is the most mobile. When I visited the Falklands Islands, I was

particularly keen to see this species. After several days of unsuccessful search-ing, I asked a local farmer where I should look. He gave me a dismissive smile and said, 'I've lived in the Falklands all my life, but I've never seen a loggerhead fly. There's no such thing as a flying logger.' ('Loggerhead' is the local name for the steamer, and refers to its large head.) He was wrong, as a couple of days later I did find my first flier, though it was swimming, rather than flying, at the time. It was a couple of miles inland, on a freshwater lake, and was clearly a smaller, more compact bird than its flightless relations.

Flightless steamer ducks

South American specials

South America is a continent rich in ducks, and it has a number of rather special species that do not fit neatly into any of the regular families. The delightful little **Brazilian duck**, or teal, is a classic example. Despite its name, it is widespread in the tropical lowland forests of South America, and occurs from eastern Colombia to northern Argentina, where I first saw it in the wild.

Even smaller than the Brazilian teal is the **ringed teal** (at 35-38 centimetres/14-15 in they are one of the tiniest of all the waterfowl); these dainty little birds are widespread (though generally scarce) through much of middle South America. Many authorities used to put the ringed teal in the same family as the perching ducks, as they do perch readily, but they are now generally regarded as an aberrant dabbling duck. They usually feed by dabbling on the surface, or putting their heads and necks under water.

Like both the Brazilian and ringed teals, the **bronze-winged** or **spectacled duck** also lacks any close relations. It is a bird of southern South America, and is restricted to Argentina and Chile, extending as far south as Tierra del Fuego. It is generally found on heavily forested rivers and fast-flowing streams, where it feeds by wading in the shallows. They are not very numerous (I

Bronze-winged duck

failed to see any during a visit to Patagonia, despite trying hard), but are easy to overlook as they do not fly much, and are unusually confiding and easy to approach.

South and Central America is also home to one of the world's most familiar ducks, the **muscovy.** Though wild muscovies are much trimmer and more athletic-looking than their domestic counterparts, they are still ugly-looking birds. Muscovies range from Mexico to northern Argentina, and are usually found on pools and lakes within the forest. When Columbus first invaded South America, he found that the native Indians had domesticated the muscovy. Today, muscovies are rare in many parts of their range, having been hunted mercilessly. The wild muscovies I have seen were wary and difficult to approach, flying readily when disturbed.

African specials

One of the least known of all the ducks is **Hartlaub's,** a bird of the forest streams of West and Central Africa. It has hardly ever been studied in the wild, and its nest has never been found. The only other duck that a wild Hartlaub's is ever likely to mix with is the **African black duck.** This bird has long been grouped with the dabbling ducks, but it displays a number of unusual characteristics which suggest that it might really be closer related to the shelducks. It is a bird of fast-flowing streams and rivers in hill country, ranging from Ethiopia to South Africa. I have always struggled to find it in Kenya, even on streams where it is known to be resident, but have found it much more readily in South Africa. Confusingly, many African birdwatchers refer to the **Cape teal** as the Cape wigeon, but it is not related to the wigeon at all. Though widely distributed over much of tropical Africa, it is often uncommon or local.

The little **Hottentot teal** is the smallest of the African ducks. Ranging from Ethiopia to South Africa, with an isolated breeding population in Nigeria and Chad, it is often common on shallow freshwater marshes and ponds. Ringing records suggest that is chiefly sedentary, rarely moving far. The Hottentot is an unobtrusive little bird, and easily overlooked. When all the other ducks on a pond have flown, the Hottentots will often remain.

Several African ducks, including the Hottentot teal, occur on the island of Madagascar, but it also has its own trio of endemic waterfowl: the **Madagascar teal,** the **Madagascar pochard** and **Meller's duck.** All three are seriously endangered, and the pochard may even be extinct.

Wood ducks

Arguably the most beautiful of all the world's waterfowl, there is no mistaking a drake **mandarin.** Ever since the first birds were imported from their native China to Britain, in about 1745, this duck has been much sought-after for wildfowl collections. A drake mandarin's plumage is a mixture of orange, gold, burgundy and blue, but the most distinctive features are the orange 'side-whiskers' and the curious golden 'sails'. The latter are modified secondary feathers, and play an important part in mandarin courtship. When displaying, the drake mandarin erects his sails and puffs out his side-whiskers, and looks like a fancy painted galleon in full sail.

In China the mandarin is now a relatively rare bird, but in Japan the annual national waterfowl counts have shown that numbers are increasing, though it remains far from abundant. (It was apparently much more common in the past.)

It is curious that the mandarin's close relation, the **Carolina wood duck**, has never succeeded in establishing itself in Britain, as it is widely kept in captivity, and full-winged birds have often been released from collections. The two species do not hybridise, as the mandarin has an unusual chromosome which prevents hybridisation with any other species.

The Carolina is a native of North America, where numbers were so depleted in the early years of this century that the species was threatened with extinction. It was then America's rarest duck, and it was said that there were more Carolinas in captivity in Europe than wild in the United States. A captive breeding programme released more than 9,000 birds in the years between the First and Second World Wars, and this was a major help in re-establishing the Carolina in its native country. Today, the Carolina is widely distributed throughout the eastern states, and can also be found quite widely to the west of the Rockies.

NOT SO FAITHFUL

The mandarin features prominently in Chinese and Japanese art and literature. According to Chinese tradition, pairs of mandarins were once given as gifts at weddings as a symbol of marital fidelity. However, mandarins do not really set a good example, as, though their pair bonds are strong, they are renewed annually, while the drake has nothing to do with the rearing of the ducklings.

Pygmy geese

Do not be misled by their name: the pygmy geese are not geese at all, but the smallest of the ducks. These dainty little birds do have a short, rather goose-like beak, but that is where the resemblance ends. There are three species of **pygmy geese**: the **green**, which occurs in northern Australia and southern New Guinea; the **cotton**, the most widely distributed of the trio, with a range

Green pygmy geese are found in tropical Australia and New Guinea

extending from India to Australia; and the **African,** which is found sporadically throughout sub-Saharan Africa and also in Madagascar. All three are delicate, tropical birds.

African pygmy geese may have a huge range, but they can be quite elusive, as they frequent lakes and pools with clear water, preferably well covered with lily pads. I have seen them at their most abundant in Botswana's Okavango delta, one of their African strongholds.

In Queensland the range of the **cotton pygmy** overlaps with the **green,** but the former is a rare bird in Australia, and much more common elsewhere in south-east Asia. I saw my first in Thailand, sitting in the tops of palm trees. Unlikely though such behaviour appears to be, it is quite normal: all three pygmy geese nest in holes in trees. Considering how widely distributed they are, pygmy geese have been little studied. The standard work on African birds, *The Birds of Africa Vol I*, describes the African pygmy goose's general habits, and breeding habits, as 'little known'. One of the reasons why these charming ducks are so little known is that they are not suited for life in captivity. They have only been kept successfully full-winged, in aviaries, and cannot stand the frosts and snow of northern Europe.

Aberrant ducks

It sounds a bit of an insult be called an aberrant duck, but a surprising number end up with this title. This is because they don't fit neatly into one of the major duck families, and the taxonomists cannot decide with which family they have the closest relationship. The New Zealand **blue duck** is a classic example, and so too are the strikingly beautiful **torrent ducks** of the Andes, which fill a similar ecological niche to the blue duck, for they like rushing rivers, and are skilled swimmers in the turbulent white waters.

In the mountains of New Guinea you can find, if you are lucky, another bird of fast-flowing rivers: **Salvadori's teal.** Arguably the least known of all the waterfowl, this is an easy bird to recognise, for both sexes share the same barred plumage. Taxonomists remain confused about this species, and whether it should be placed in the genus *Anas*, or in its own *Salvadorina*; current thinking tends towards the latter view.

As well as having more than its fair share of unusual mammals, Australia can also boast several extraordinary ducks. My favourite is the **pink-eared**, which really does have a pink smudge behind the ear. However, the pink-eared's most obvious feature is its huge beak – much the biggest beak in proportion to its body size of any of the wildfowl. The strangest of Australia's endemic ducks, and certainly the rarest, is the **freckled**. Studies of its anatomical features suggest that it is more closely related to the swans than any of the other ducks, while the lack of patterning of the downy ducklings is unique among dabbling ducks. When I first visited eastern Australia I was delighted to find that the **maned duck** or **Australian wood duck** was a common bird in parks and botanical gardens, where it competes with the black ducks for bread from visitors. In the outback it is a different story, for the maned duck is a popular sporting quarry, and tends to be wild and wary as a result. The maned duck is not a great swimmer, and spends most of its time on land, where it walks and runs with ease.

Torrent duck, a bird of fast flowing rivers in the Andes

Australian maned ducks, also known as maned geese

Pink-eared duck, a widespread species throughout Australia

Most books on ducks group the **African white-backed duck** with the stifftails, simply because it looks like one. However, current thinking suggests that this grebe-like bird is a distant cousin of the whistling ducks. I have seen white-backed ducks on several occasions, but never learnt much about them, as they spend most of the day sleeping among lily pads.

The **knob-billed** or **comb duck** can often be found on the same pans or pools as the white-backed, but the two could hardly be more different in appearance or behaviour. The knobby looks more like a goose than a duck, and is not the sort of bird that wins beauty contests. It has a similar distribution to the fulvous whistling duck, for it can be found throughout much of the tropics in Africa, South America and Asia. The breeding behaviour is also unusual, for the drake will take two or more wives, whom he will defend vigorously from intruding males.

The **white-winged wood duck** could rightfully complain about being called an aberrant duck, as it does have a relation in the forests of the South America – the muscovy. Like the latter, it is a bird of forest swamps and pools, but it is exceedingly rare and elusive, and difficult to see despite its size, which is about the same as a wild muscovy.

Mallard group

There is no doubt that the **mallard** is the world's most successful duck. Though it is strictly a bird of the temperate north, ranging widely through North America, Europe and Asia, its descendants have colonised many other areas, from remote offshore islands to whole continents. The mallard owes much of its success to its adaptability, as it is quite happy to live alongside man, even in parks in the middle of large cities. Here it becomes very tame, in contrast to its wary rural cousins, whose very survival depends on avoiding the man with the gun. Mallard are second only to the pheasant as the sportsman's favourite quarry, and as a result have been introduced into many countries where they are not native. (See Aliens, p. 86)

Pacific black ducks, the Australian counterpart of the mallard

In New Guinea, Australia and New Zealand, the **Pacific black duck** represents the mallard family, in India and south-east Asia it is the **spotbill**, and in the Philippines the **Philippine duck**. In Africa, it is the **yellow-billed duck** which takes the mallard's place, though on the island of Madagascar **Meller's duck** fills the role. Mallard rarely migrate far into Africa, so yellow-bills and mallards are unlikely to come into contact with each other. Similarly, yellow-bills do not occur in Madagascar. The only gap in the mallard group's bid for world domination is South America, where there are no mallard-like representatives.

Pintail

If there was a prize for the world's most elegant duck, then a drake **northern pintail** would be a likely winner. The pintail is widespread throughout the northern hemisphere, and is particularly numerous in North America, where the autumn population may sometimes exceed 10 million birds. In Britain it is one of our scarcer ducks, seldom found in large flocks except in a few favoured localities such as the estuary of the River Mersey. As its athletic looks suggest, it is a fast flier, a good walker and a buoyant swimmer – the perfect all-round duck. Pintail are also good socialisers, happiest in their own company (when they sometimes form flocks thousands strong), but also ready to mix with other dabbling ducks such as mallard and wigeon. The northern pintail has a South American cousin, the **yellow-billed pintail**, but the African **red-billed pintail** (or teal) is a more distant relation.

Wigeon

With their similar shape, habits and behaviour, the world's three species of wigeon – the European, American and Chiloe – are all closely related. Much the most widespread is the **European** or **Eurasian wigeon**, which breeds throughout northern Europe and Asia, and is an abundant wintering bird in Britain. Small numbers do nest in the British Isles, mainly in northern Scotland but occasionally farther south. Wigeon are grazing ducks, their short beaks perfectly adapted for grazing, goose-like, on short grass on the banks of reservoirs, lakes or rivers. The rather drably plumaged gadwall, and the exotic-looking falcated duck, are both distant cousins of the wigeon.

Pintail, the world's most elegant duck?

Wigeon, a widespread species throughout Europe and Asia

Tufted duck, a typical diving duck

Shovelers and blue-wings

Thanks to their curious, shovel-shaped beaks, the shovelers are among the easiest of ducks to identify. There are four species of shoveler, all of which are similar in size, but have different colouring and markings, and ranges that do not overlap. The **northern shoveler** has by far the widest distribution, breeding throughout the northern hemisphere. Though many wintering birds stay in Europe and the USA, others go to the northern tropics.

Common to all four shoveler species is a distinctive blue forewing, a feature also found in three species of teal: the **garganey**, the **cinnamon** and the **blue-wing**. This trio of ducks are all closely related to the shovelers, with similar diets, though less-specialised feeding habits.

Teal

Teal is a loose term, applied to the majority of the small dabbling ducks. The standard **teal**, if one can have such a bird, is the green-winged teal of the northern hemisphere. It is one of the most widely distributed of ducks, and nests throughout much of Britain. The teal has its counterparts in most parts of the world. In South America the **speckled teal** takes its place. In Australasia, the most widespread and most numerous of ducks is the **grey teal**. The **chestnut teal** is an Australian endemic, occurring mainly in south-eastern Australia (it is Tasmania's most numerous duck), with a smaller population in Western Australia. It is a bird of coastal lagoons and mangrove swamps (which is where I saw my first birds in southern Queensland), but also occurs inland on freshwater lakes and ponds.

Diving ducks

Mallard, teal, wigeon and shoveler are all surface-feeding ducks, finding most of their food by dabbling or upending. In contrast, the diving ducks plunge underwater for their food, and as result have a different shape. All have their legs placed farther back in the body, but though this makes diving much easier, it makes walking rather more awkward. Taking off from the water is also more difficult. Whereas the surface feeders all spring from the water, the divers have to make a running take-off, pattering along the water until they get airborne.

There are 15 members of this group, and they divide roughly into four. The familiar **tufted duck** represents the black and white divers, which also includes the **ring-necked duck** and two species of **scaup**. The European **pochard**, with its grey body and red head, has two look-alikes in North

Pochard scratching

Drake hooded merganser, handsome North American sawbills

America, the **canvasback** and the **redhead**. Then there are the white-eyes, such as the **ferruginous duck**, with reddish-brown plumage and distinctive white eyes. Odd ducks out are the handsome **red-crested pochard** and its South American cousin, the **rosybill**.

Sawbills
This highly distinctive and specialist family of fish-eating ducks has six members, only one of which (the exceedingly rare **Brazilian merganser**) occurs in the Southern Hemisphere. However, two breed in Britain – the **red-breasted merganser** and **goosander** – while a third (the **smew**) is a rare but regular wintering bird.

Sea ducks
Everybody has heard of the **eider duck**. The common eider is one of the most distinctive of ducks, and readily identifiable by its shape and size in any plumage. Though eiders do occur regularly around the coast of southern England, you have to travel north to see them in any numbers. They are among the most confiding of ducks, so one can often sit and watch them at close range. The common eider is much the commonest and most widespread of the world's four species of eider, occurring on coastal waters of the Arctic and sub-Arctic. Eiders are highly sociable, and are usually found in flocks, while they are also unusual in that they nest in colonies. Eider down, plucked from the mother duck's breast to line her nest, has long been valued

An eider on her nest, lined with down plucked from her breast

by man – see Plumage (p. 72). Eiders dive for their food, which is mainly made up of molluscs (such as mussels) and crustaceans (such as starfish and shorecrabs).

The **scoters** are related to the eiders, and in most bird books you will find the two on the same page. Most British birdwatchers know scoters as the rather mysterious black ducks they usually see flying out at sea, invariably in fast-moving packs low over the water. In the winter you seldom see a single scoter, as these are highly gregarious birds.

Much more distinctive in their plumage than the scoters are the three species of goldeneye. Only one of the trio occurs in Britain: the **common goldeneye**. This handsome duck is widely distributed throughout the northern hemisphere. Goldeneye are hole-nesting birds, and in Europe they favour nesting in old black woodpecker nest cavities, in North America pileated woodpecker holes are favoured. They will nest readily in boxes, and it is the provision of nest boxes in Scotland that has established a British breeding population (see Eggs, p.40). The distinctive **harlequin** duck is also included in the sea duck group, though it spends its summers on fast-flowing rivers. Harlequins rarely reach Britain, unlike the Arctic-nesting **long-tailed duck**, which is a common wintering bird on the coasts of Scotland.

Laysan teal are often regarded as a sub-species of the mallard

Species or sub-species?

Many different species of ducks are very similar in appearance and behaviour but have evolved into separate species due to isolation. However, many taxonomists cannot agree on whether some ducks deserve full specific status, or should be regarded as mere sub-species of their ancestral duck. Take the **Laysan teal** as an example. This diminutive island duck is quite clearly a descendant of the mallard. Many thousands of years ago a pair of mallard managed to reach Laysan Island, where they stayed and bred. Isolation and lack of competition from other ducks led to the drakes eventually losing their bright plumage, while other factors (such as poor feeding conditions) led to the small size. Laysan teal and mallard are quite capable of hybridising together, and producing fertile offspring, but the Laysan teal's isolation on its Pacific island has prevented such hybridisation taking place, except in captivity. Thus today most taxonomists grant the Laysan teal full specific status, while other regard it as simply a race, or sub-species, of mallard.

There are several other ducks that have clearly descended from the mallard, but which in isolation from mallard blood have evolved separately. Other examples include the **Hawaiian duck** (and possibly this bird is the most recent ancestor of the Laysan teal); the **Mariana mallard** (now possibly extinct), and several ducks found in the eastern and southern parts of North America. For some reason the mallard was virtually absent from the eastern states of the USA, and here its place was taken by the closely related **black**

A chestnut teal drake, a close relative of the grey teal

duck. In the south-eastern USA, and adjacent Mexico, you find the **mottled duck**, which appears to be intermediate between the mallard and the black duck, and the very similar **Mexican duck**. American birdwatchers regard the latter as simply a race of the mallard, but give full species status to the mottled duck.

Chestnut teal and **grey teal** are closely related, and the two species are often found together in the wild in Australia. Though they will hybridise readily in captivity, they are not thought to do so in the wild. However, it has been suggested that the resulting hybrids would be so difficult to pick out that hybridisation may occur more often than is generally thought.

It is not just with the mallard complex that the problem of sub-species occurs. Take also the pintail group. **Pintail** are great migrants, regularly turning up in out-of-the-way places like Hawaii, and sometimes as far south as South Africa and Borneo. **Eaton's pintail**, or the **Kerguelen pintail**, is almost certainly descended from a pair or two of lost, migrant pintail that somehow managed to reach the island of Kerguelen, in the southern Indian Ocean. Thousands of years of evolution have resulted in a small pintail in which the sexes are similar in appearance, both resembling a duck northern pintail. Occasionally a slightly brighter drake appears, showing some of the markings of its northern pintail ancestry. Eaton's pintail is generally regarded as a sub-species of the northern pintail. This duck has been successfully introduced to St Paul and Amsterdam Islands, while another, very similar, pintail also occurs on Crozet Island (all in the Indian Ocean).

The **teal** has its counterparts in most parts of the world. In South America the **speckled teal** takes its place. There are four races of this small brown duck. The most widespread are usually known as the **yellow-billed teal**, and they occur throughout much of southern South America, extending high into the Andes, and across to the Falklands. As their name suggests, they have a bright yellow beak, their most obvious distinguishing feature. The northern races of the speckled teal are known as the **Andean teal**, and they lack the yellow beak, and are rather duller in colour. The ranges of the yellow-billed and Andean teals do not overlap, adding weight to the argument that the two types should be regarded as separate species.

Most duck experts recognise three species of scoters: **common** (or black), **surf** and **velvet**. However, the velvet scoter is sometimes split into two, with the birds breeding in Eastern Asia and North America called the **white-winged scoter**. The latter differ from their European counterparts by having orange rather than yellow bills, which are also rather more swollen in appearance during the breeding season. Other subtle differences have also been recognised, though there is no doubt that the velvet/white-winged scoters are very closely related to each other.

DUCK NAMES

On the whole, most English duck names are fairly easy to understand, as they often describe a duck's appearance, or its voice. A tufted duck does indeed have a tuft, and a goldeneye does have a golden eye, though (confusingly) so does the former. Thus a degree of caution is always essential when matching names to ducks. However, the origin of many English names is obscure or confused, while most French duck names, for example, are much easier to understand.

The French call the mallard the *canard colvert* (green-necked duck), which makes sense, while our word mallard is derived from a mixture of Latin, Old French and High German. It is interesting to note that 'mallard' was widely used in the Middle Ages, but fell from fashion in the 19th and first half of the 20th century. Only a drake was called a mallard, and otherwise this species was simply known as the wild duck.

The mallard is far from the only duck whose name has foreign roots. The name 'garganey' is derived from the Italian *garganello*, which was apparently first used by the German-Swiss naturalist Conrad Gesner in his book *Historiae Animalium*, a work much referred to by 17th-century British ornithologists. A much simpler name for the garganey is 'summer teal', and this is what the French call it (*sarcelle d'été*). Logically, the French call the teal the *sarcelle d'hiver*, and the Baikal teal the *sarcelle élégante*. The latter makes

Baikal teal are recorded only rarely on Lake Baikal

Red-billed pintail are also known as red-billed teal

a great deal of sense, as Baikal teal are rarely recorded on Lake Baikal. (When I visited Lake Baikal I saw my first falcated teal instead.)

A number of ducks have alternative English names that are now seldom used, or have almost been forgotten. A northern English name for the pintail was 'thin neck', which hardly does such an elegant bird justice. Rather more satisfactory, and still occasionally used, is 'sea pheasant', though the latter can cause confusion with the long-tailed duck, which is also sometimes called this. It is hardly surprising that the shoveler has a variety of names, as its distinctive appearance lends itself to descriptive labels. 'Spoon bill' is quite logical, but there is already another bird of the same name.

Whistling ducks really do whistle, but many of this family are still called 'tree ducks', despite the fact that some never perch, and others never go near trees. The name tree duck is continued in a number of modern field guides, though most have now switched across to whistling duck.

Descriptive names can cause problems. There are three ducks called, simply, 'black duck': one in North America, one in Africa and the other in Australia. They are all different species, and not one of them is really black. As a result, in a book like this, each gets labelled by its continent of origin, hence North American black duck and African black duck. Local birdwatchers carry on calling them black ducks.

Equally confusing is the fact that in Europe we simply have a teal, a pintail and a shoveler, but when you travel to South America, for example, you find there is a speckled teal, a yellow-billed pintail and an Argentine (or red) shoveler. In South Africa, there is a red-billed pintail (or teal), a Cape shoveler and a Cape teal. To avoid confusion, there is a case for tacking the word Eurasian on to the familiar teal, as it occurs throughout Europe and Asia, but the word northern will suffice for both pintail and shoveler, as the two occur throughout the northern hemisphere.

Many of the ducks that occur in Europe are also found in North America, and they usually share the same English name. However, there are some notable exceptions. The velvet scoter becomes (logically enough) the white-winged scoter, and the goosander is generally known as the common (or even American) merganser. The long-tailed duck is invariably known as the old squaw, as the loud noise it makes is said to resemble an old squaw nagging her husband. Americans always call the Carolina wood duck just plain wood duck, but as it is such a pretty bird I much prefer to call it a Carolina, or Carolina wood duck. Americans often slip a 'd' into wigeon, making it widgeon. This probably comes from an old English spelling, but, like pidgeon for pigeon, is somewhat antiquated.

There is one American name widely used by British birdwatchers: green-winged teal. Most birders, when they refer to a green-winged teal, are talking about the North American race of teal, *Anas crecca carolinensis*. Its wings are just as green as the teal we see in Europe, and the Americans only call it that to differentiate it from the blue-winged teal. However, the drake *carolinensis* does have subtle plumage differences from the European race, and the two are easy to tell apart in the field. Not so the females, which are identical.

Whether duck names, or any other bird names for that matter, should have capital letters is a much debated subject. I prefer to avoid capitals

Long-tailed duck, known in North America as 'old squaw'

whenever possible, and only use one when a proper name is included in the duck's name (such as Barrow's goldeneye or Laysan teal). However, most British bird magazines use capital letters for bird names, even though the RSPB does not in its magazine *Birds*. The pro-capitals lobby argue that a Yellow-billed Duck, for example, is quite clearly the African duck *Anas undulata*, but a yellow-billed duck could be anything from a drake mallard to a drake Salvadori's duck. It is a good argument, but I work on the basis that only proper names need capitals, and duck names, like plant names, do not come into this category.

Whenever there is any doubt or confusion about a duck's name, then it is best to use the scientific name, which is based on Latin. The first half of the scientific name identifies the genus (the family of which the duck is a member), the second half the individual species. Thus it is obvious from their scientific names that both teal, *Anas crecca*, and pintail, *Anas acuta*, are related, but the second name is unique to each bird. When sub-species are involved, then a third name is usually added to the existing two, hence *Anas crecca carolinensis* for the North American race of teal. Once a bird has been given a scientific name, it usually keeps it for ever after, but changes in taxonomy can lead to changes in the scientific name. Thus the rather strange Salvadori's teal is generally known as *Salvadorina waigiuensis*, but some authors refer to it as *Anas waigiuensis*. Fortunately, there are relatively few ducks which the taxonomists cannot agree about, so this is an unusual exception to the general rule.

From eggs to ducklings

EGGS

Compared with the beautifully marked eggs laid by so many birds, duck eggs are boring. Not a single duck lays a spotted or marked egg, and the colour of the shell ranges simply from white to olive green. Nor is there much variety in shape: ducks eggs are invariably oval, with one end only slightly more pointed than the other. What all duck eggs have in common is their mass: they are very large in proportion to the size of the bird that lays them. This is because ducklings hatch from the egg in an advanced state, able to swim and feed themselves, almost as soon as they have hatched. In technical terms, ducks are known as 'precocial' species, and the ducklings are 'nidifugous'. (The opposites are 'altricial' and 'nidicolous'.)

Most ducks lay one egg a day, usually early in the morning. The size of the clutch varies from species to species. The majority lay between eight and a dozen eggs, while ducks that live on small islands (such as Laysan teal) usually lay smaller clutches. Most of the South American ducks tend to lay smaller clutches than their northern counterparts, with torrent ducks producing one of the smallest clutches of all waterfowl – a mere three to four eggs at a time. Stifftails also lay small clutches, with the curious musk duck from Australia producing the least of all. Just one to three eggs make up a musk duck clutch. In the northern hemisphere ducks lay in the spring, in the southern hemisphere in the austral spring, and in the Tropics they lay when the weather is suitable – which is when it rains.

Ducks are unusual in the bird world in that they do not make nests. The eggs are usually laid on the ground in a hollow, often among thick vegetation. The sitting duck may peck and move the surrounding vegetation, but ducks lack the instinct to carry nesting material. The nest itself is lined with down from the mother's breast, a habit unique to waterfowl.

Most ducks nest close to water, while some (particularly the stifftails) like to lay their eggs in aquatic, floating vegetation. Stifftails find walking very difficult, so it is obviously essential to have the nest as close to water as possible. In contrast, certain species seem happier nesting well away from water. Northern pintail, for example, will often nest up to a mile from water. Even more surprising are the tree-nesting ducks such as goldeneye, smew and bufflehead. These birds like to nest in tree cavities, or even old woodpecker holes, though if trees are not available most (though not all) will lay their eggs under boulders or in similar sites. Competition for suitable

Mallard and ducklings

A female goosander at her tree-hole nest site

nesting trees can be intense, and where the breeding ranges of goldeneye and hooded merganser overlap, it is not unusual for mixed clutches to be laid.

Several other species of ducks, ranging from mandarins to Australian wood ducks, also like to nest in trees, sometimes high above the ground. The African pygmy goose favours trees if it can find them, but there are records of these tiny ducks nesting in termite mounds, even in the roofs of thatched houses. As with all ducks, a degree of adaptability is essential for survival.

Unlike geese, which can be very aggressive, ducks are generally inoffensive and unable to defend their nest from predators. As a result they are extremely good at hiding their nests, making the most of even sparse vegetation to hide the eggs completely.

NO 'PECKERS, NO HOLES

In Scandinavia, most goldeneye nest in abandoned black woodpecker holes. Black woodpeckers do not occur in Scotland, so until 25 years ago no goldeneyes nested there, due to a lack of suitable nest sites. Then, in the early '70s, goldeneye nest boxes were erected around many potential breeding lochs. The goldeneye took to them at once, and at least 200 female goldeneye now nest in Scotland, with the population centred around Speyside.

An incomplete clutch of teal eggs

THE CUCKOO DUCK

Just one duck behaves in the manner of the cuckoo. This is the aberrant black-headed duck. Though a member of the stifftail family, it does not really look like a stifftail at all, and its links with the family may be tenuous. What makes it interesting is its nesting behaviour, or rather its lack of nesting behaviour, for the black-headed is totally nest parasitic, which means that it never incubates its own eggs. The female lays her eggs in the nests of other waterbirds, and lets the host do the incubation. Though rosy-billed pochards and red shovelers are the favoured hosts, black-headed duck eggs have been found in the nests of 18 different species, ranging from coots to snail kites. The eggs are programmed to hatch at the same time as those of the host species (the piping of the host's eggs sets off a hatching response in the black-head egg), but, once hatched, the duckling leaves its host and is totally independent. One adaptation for this unusual start to life is a thick coat of down, which makes up for the duckling not being brooded by its mother. Black-headed ducks are reputed to be quite common in their restricted South American range, but they are both shy and inconspicuous, making them easy to overlook. One of the most reliable sites for them is the wetland reserve of Costanera Sur, in the heart of Buenos Aires, which is where I saw my first individuals.

DUCKLINGS

As ducklings must all leave the nest at the same time, it is essential that incubation starts simultaneously. Thus the mother duck does not start to sit on the eggs until she has completed her clutch, and this is also when she first lines the nest with her down. The down helps keep the eggs warm when she leaves the nest. Some species of ducks do not feed throughout the incubation period, but most will slip off the eggs once a day to feed, bathe and preen. With the notable exception of the whistling ducks, incubation is exclusively a chore for the female. The whistling ducks are unusual in that both parents incubate, and also look after the ducklings, just like the swans and geese.

Incubation is a lengthy task, for most duck eggs take at least 28 days to hatch. However, some of the small ducks do have shorter incubation periods – just 21 days in the case of teal – while others are considerably longer. The female muscovy, for example, must sit for 35 days before her eggs hatch, though such a lengthy period is unusual.

The synchrony of the hatch is not simply due to incubation commencing at the same moment. We now know that the developing embryos communicate with each other (and with their mother) with clicks and low-frequency vibrations, and this helps to synchronise the hatching. Breaking out of the egg is hard work, and it takes most ducklings anything from 16 to 24 hours to finally emerge.

Mallard turning eggs

As soon as the brood have all hatched and their down has dried, the mother duck leads them off to water. In the case of hole-nesting species, such as goldeneye and mandarins, the ducklings are born with a strong climbing ability, and clamber instinctively to the entrance of the nest hole. From here they simply launch themselves into space, instinctively flapping their tiny wings. They are sufficiently light that they can parachute down from holes as high as 25 metres (82 feet) above the ground without being harmed.

The duckling's natal down lasts for only a brief period – seldom much more than a week. It is replaced with a denser (and drabber) soft down. Soon the first feathers start to emerge on the wings and the body, with the down on the head, neck and back the last to disappear. Most ducks are fully fledged and able to fly by eight weeks, with their first plumage resembling that of their mother. The majority of young drakes will acquire their first full breeding plumage later in the autumn, but some species (such as the eiders) take at least two years before acquiring their complete breeding finery.

Ducklings are able to feed themselves from the moment they hatch, randomly pecking at anything that takes their fancy. Their mother plays no part in feeding them, though she does conduct her brood to good feeding areas. While the majority of adult ducks

JUST SHUT YOUR EYES AND JUMP!

Mallard and ducklings

are mainly vegetarian, ducklings require a high protein diet which includes a great deal of insect food. Though the mother duck may not feed her brood, she does play a crucially important role in keeping her brood together and stopping them from scattering too widely. This is vital when it comes to avoiding predators, as the more scattered the ducklings, the more vulnerable they are to being taken by crows, foxes and other creatures that relish eating ducklings. The mother duck's other important job is to brood her ducklings, and prevent them from becoming chilled. The danger period for chilling passes after the first week, though sudden and unexpected cold weather can still kill even large ducklings.

Once the ducklings have fledged, any ties between the young birds and their mother are broken. This is in marked contrast to the geese and swans, in which the young of the year stay with their parents for the coming autumn and winter.

CRECHE

If you see a pair of shelduck with 30 or even 40 ducklings, you can be pretty sure that this is the result of several families combining together, for shelduck favour a crèche system for rearing their young. Sometimes as many as 100 ducklings will gather together, and these are usually looked after by some of their parents. Quite what happens to the absent parents no-one knows for sure. It seems likely that some of the ducks simply lose their broods when the parties of ducklings become mixed up, while perhaps certain adults are quite pleased to shed their parental responsibilities.

A QUESTION OF SURVIVAL

Part of the mallard's success can be attributed to its ability to produce large numbers of ducklings. It is not unusual to see mallard ducklings in England in early March, though the first broods are rarely successful. Ducklings hatched in late April or May are more likely to survive to maturity. Every year, a few broods of wild mallard are seen in the autumn, but not many of these late ducklings survive. The mallard drakes have nothing to do with the rearing of the ducklings, which is the duck's sole responsibility. The ducklings leave the nest within 14 to 21 hours of hatching, and will stay with their mother until they fledge, some 50 to 60 days later. If small ducklings become separated from their mother their chances of survival are poor, but partly fledged ducklings may well survive, especially in areas where predators are few, and food plentiful.

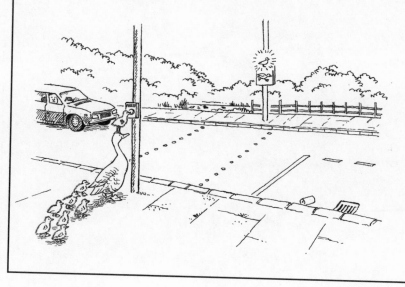

On the move

RESIDENTS

If you think you recognise an individual mallard on the village pond as the same bird that has been there for the past eight years, you may well be right. Individual mallard can be remarkably faithful to one site, never moving far from it. Mallard are not generally thought of as being highly migratory, but if you check the statistics you discover that more than one third of British wintering mallard are immigrants, and they come from a very wide area of northern Europe and Russia. Thus Britain's mallard can be described as a mixed bunch, made up largely of residents (who may move around the country), and winter immigrants.

Sedentary ducks that never move far from where they were hatched are unusual, but they certainly exist. No duck shows less migratory instinct than the Laysan teal. Laysan is a tiny, isolated volcanic island in the Pacific; it measures just 1.8 miles (3km) by .93 miles (1.5km). The nearest land of any note is the north-western chain of Hawaiian islands, some 139 miles (225km) away. In the middle of Laysan Island is a brackish central lagoon, and this is the centre for the entire population of wild Laysan teal. At one stage the population dropped to a single female, but she managed to lay fertile eggs, and today the number of teal on Laysan may be as high as 500 birds.

Most of the other island-dwelling ducks, such as the Falkland Island steamer, the Madagascar teal, the Auckland Islands brown teal, even the Philippine duck, are equally sedentary. So, too, are a small number of other species, mostly those found in the Tropics, and where their habitat changes little in character throughout the year. The little-known Hartlaub's duck lives along streams in the rainforests of Zaire and surrounding countries, and seldom moves any distance during its life. Another African duck, the curious little white-backed, is also described as being sedentary, but as it has a liking for temporary pans (pools which flood seasonally) it is forced to move around. The specialised habitats of the torrent ducks and the blue duck from New Zealand, also mean that they seldom move far. However, the blue duck does have a large territory, which it moves around in freely.

FLIGHT

Many thousands of years ago, the South American steamer ducks gave up flying. They simply got too big and heavy to get into the air, while a sedentary life style and a lack of predators meant that flying was an unnecessary extravagance. Being unable to fly meant restricting themselves to the coast, and allowed the very similar flying steamer duck to exploit inland habitats. Flying and flightless steamer ducks can, and do, occur together, but with

Pintail flying in V formation

practice they are quite easy to tell apart. The latter is a lighter, more elegant bird, while it has visibly longer wings (see p. 14).

Steamer ducks take their name from the fact that they 'steam' across the water when in a hurry; flying steamer ducks also have to steam across the water in order to get airborne. Such a laborious take-off is typical of most diving ducks, which are forced to patter along for some distance before gaining flight speed. Stifftails are all reluctant fliers, preferring to escape from danger by diving or swimming away. As a result they seldom feature in wildfowlers' bags. If they do decide to fly, then a great deal of pattering along the water is needed before getting airborne. Once up, their flight is rapid, with whirring wing beats. In contrast, most surface-feeding ducks can spring into the air, even launching themselves almost vertically, like a rocket, if suddenly surprised.

Some ducks are considerably better at flying than others. The most agile are the small ducks, like the mandarin and North American Carolina wood duck, that can fly easily between the branches of trees in their favoured

---

WHISTLING WINGS

Identifying flying ducks by sound, rather than sight, is possible with both the goldeneye and Steller's eider. Both species have wings that whistle in flight, though in the case of the goldeneye it is only the drake whose wings produce the characteristic whistling sound. Both sexes of Steller's eider have whistling wings, and the whistle is said to be louder than that of the goldeneye.

wooded habitat. Whistling ducks, with their broad wings, are also flexible fliers. However, only a minority of ducks display such agility. Most species have small wings and heavy bodies, which reduces the scope for manoeuvrability. Few other birds have such a low ratio of wing-surface area to body weight. Ducks make up for this handicap by being exceptionally powerful fliers, those broad breasts supplying the muscle to allow the wings to beat at a very fast rate. In level flight a small duck, such as a teal, may beat its wings at a rate of more than 300 strokes a minute. Such propulsion makes ducks among the fastest-flying of all birds, at least in level flight. Few other birds, and certainly not swifts and swallows, can outpace an eider, which might reach 60 mph in level flight, and is arguably the world's fastest bird. A more normal cruising speed for most ducks is probably about 30 mph.

Even flying at 30 mph requires a great deal of energy. Migrating wildfowl can at least stop on the sea for a rest, but they also employ energy-saving methods to reduce the flying effort required. Formation flying is the secret – by flying in V-formation, members of the flock can make considerable savings in the effort required to keep the wings beating. For the technically minded, they do this by flying just outside the wing-tip vortices created by their neighbours (a form of slip-streaming). At cruising speed this allows a 15% saving in the aerodynamic power needed. No-one yet knows how the lead duck is chosen, or how long he or she remains at the front before letting another member of the flock take over. Almost all the migratory species of wildfowl fly in formation.

There is not a great deal of information available as to how high ducks fly. On migration it seems likely that many surface-feeding species (such as wigeon and pintail) reach heights of around 3,000 metres (10,000 feet). In contrast, migrating scoters and eiders usually fly just a few feet above the surface of the sea, rising and falling with the waves.

'IT WAS A LONG WAY TO COME, BUT THE WEATHER'S PERFECT!'

MIGRATION

Ducks are among the avian world's greatest migrants, with many species travelling thousands of miles during their lives. The majority of the ducks that winter in Britain are migrants from overseas. Ringing has revealed the major breeding grounds for each of the species which winters in Britain. We know, for example, that most of our pintail breed in western Siberia, but our wintering wigeon are drawn from a much wider area, including Iceland, Scandinavia and northern Russia. As most Icelandic wigeon winter in Britain, then it would make sense for Iceland's long-tailed ducks to do likewise, but they don't. Instead, they move across to Greenland, and the long-tails which reach our shores have travelled from Scandinavia and north-west Russia. In contrast, the few garganey that nest in Britain spend their winters in tropical Africa, most likely in Senegal.

Migration is a risky business, and birds only undertake it if they have good reason to do so. For most northern ducks, the tundra of the far north provide relatively safe and undisturbed breeding grounds, with an abundance of insect life for the ducklings to feed on. The clouds of mosquitoes which make life so unbearable for humans during summer provide an unlimited supply of food. However, as soon as the brief Arctic summer begins to fade, it is time for these Arctic nesting birds to be on the move again, moving south to milder wintering grounds. The southward migration will start as early as August, and by September the first returning birds will appear on the estuaries of Britain. Some of these will be heading for wintering grounds farther south, perhaps in France, Spain or North Africa, while others will remain in the same area throughout the winter, and well into the following spring. The lengthening day triggers the instinct to head back north to the breeding grounds, which are only occupied for three months of the year.

Of the northern ducks, some species are much more migratory than others. Mallard, for example, do occur widely in North Africa, but rarely penetrate farther south, unlike both shoveler and pintail. Of the North American ducks, the blue-winged teal is the most migratory, with much of the population wintering in Central and South America, and some stragglers reaching Argentina and Chile. Vagrant blue-winged teal have been recorded on many oceanic islands, from Hawaii to the Azores, and apparently wild birds are recorded annually in the British Isles.

While the northern ducks migrate in response to the changing length of the day, the movements of tropical ducks are dictated by the rains. Some species (particularly the whistling ducks) will move hundreds of miles in search of freshly flooded areas, and make regular migratory movements during the year. Other ducks, such as the African pygmy geese, are essentially nomadic, simply wandering around a wide area, with no regular pattern to their movements. Like its northern cousin, the red-billed pintail is also a considerable traveller, moving in response to the rains. Birds ringed in Zambia have been recovered in Botswana, Namibia, South Africa and Zimbabwe. The longest distance a ringed red-billed pintail has been recorded to cover is around 1,000 miles (1,600km).

Wintering ducks are quick to respond to sudden spells of freezing weather, and hard-weather movements are a typical part of duck behaviour. Rather

than endure frozen lakes, ponds or estuaries, ducks will move to milder areas. Thus a major freeze in the Low Countries will push thousands of ducks across the North Sea to England. Should the weather be bad there too, many of the birds will carry on moving west or south. Studies have shown that the ducks tend to be less hardy than the drakes, and they are quicker to move to milder areas. As a result, the flocks that remain behind may hold as many as 70% drakes. This explains why the majority of smew recorded in England are females (known as red-heads), and it is only when the weather is really cold in Holland that many drakes move across to join them.

FLYWAYS

The concept of flyways comes from North America, where migratory wildfowl were long thought to funnel down migratory corridors, such as the Mississippi Flyway, and the Atlantic Flyway. However, more recent studies of migrating flocks, using radar, have revealed that the birds use much broader areas of airspace. Thus the avian concept of a crowded M25 does not really ring true, though the term flyway remains in common usage.

Fox stalking an unsuspecting mallard

Populations

LONGEVITY

The most tricky time in a duck's life is the first three weeks. Duckling mortality is dreadfully high, which explains why most ducks have such large families in the first place. If you hatch a dozen ducklings, then there is a fair chance of at least one surviving to adulthood. Ornithologists have worked out that between 60 and 75% of the annual hatch is lost in the first year, with a worrying 90 to 95% gone within three years. However, those pondwise ducks that get through the first three years may well survive for many more. The record lifespan I have managed to find for a wild mallard is an amazing 29 years, with the eider trailing well behind on 18, and tufted duck on 15. However, it is likely that the average eider lives much longer than the equivalent mallard. Eiders do not breed until they are at least two, and possibly three years old, while their average clutch of between four and eight eggs contrasts with the mallard's dozen or more. Mallard breed in their first year, and have more young, to keep their population stable.

In captivity, where ducks are protected from predators and do not have to worry where the next meal is coming from, survival rates are much higher. Most captive ducks – even the smallest species – can expect to reach eight or nine years, while many will go on for much longer.

Most of our knowledge of wild duck ages come from ringing, but individual wild ducks are often very faithful to one wintering area, returning to the same pond or lake year after year. Without rings it is usually impossible to recognise these individuals, as they blend into the flock, but where a rare species is involved, identification is made simple. Wintering ring-necked ducks in Britain have often returned to the same gravel pit year after year – as the ring-neck is a North American species, we can be reasonably confident that the same bird has returned each winter. In Scotland, Steller's eiders are extremely rare, so we can be sure that the drake, first seen off Westray, Orkney, in October 1972, was the same bird that remained in the area until 1982. Remarkably, another Steller's eider drake was recorded off Vorran Island, South Uist (in the Outer Hebrides) from July 1972 through to 1983. The highlight of the latter's lonely life must have been on April 13th, 1974, when two female Steller's eiders joined him. One assumes that he died in 1983, but he might well have moved north, in search of the company of his own species.

Arctic fox with eider duckling

NUMBERS

As you might expect, the mallard is probably the world's most abundant duck. It certainly is in the Western Palearctic, with an estimated population of between 4 and 5 million. It is also No. 1 in North America, where there may be as many as 12 million. The world No. 2 is likely to be the northern pintail. The North American population fluctuates between 5 and 10 million birds, while the Eurasian population can probably also be counted in millions. Other abundant ducks include the lesser and greater scaups. In the summer in North America, it has been estimated that the combined populations of these two species is larger than that of any other duck except the mallard.

In Britain we regard the king eider as a rare bird, which it is in British waters. However, most king eiders occur in remote areas far from humans, and it is probably one of the world's most numerous ducks. The North American population includes at least a million in the central and western Canadian Arctic, at least 100,000 in the eastern Arctic and Greenland, and another 10,000 along the Arctic slope of Alaska. Add in the vast Siberian population and you have an abundant duck.

As the chapter on endangered ducks makes clear, there are a worrying number of species with critically low populations. Britain's rarest regular breeding duck is the garganey. Despite their rarity (probably fewer than 50 breeding pairs), they are quite easy to see at their favoured sites. The bird reserves of Titchwell and Cley in Norfolk, Minsmere and Warbleswick in Suffolk, and Elmley and Stodmarsh in Kent are all reliable places to see them. In my experience, garganey are at their most abundant in southern Siberia, where every small lake or pond seemed to hold a pair in early June. They are very gregarious in winter, and flocks thousands strong are regularly recorded on their wintering grounds in west Africa and India.

PREDATORS

If you are a duck, you have to face the fact that you live in an unfriendly world. Everyone wants to eat you, or, if they can't catch you, they will eat your eggs and ducklings. Duck predators come in all shapes and sizes, from man to mink, pike to polecat. In Britain, the main duck predators, apart from man, are foxes, mink and rats, though almost any carnivore will tackle an unwary duck if it gets the chance. Duck eggs are particularly popular, and are not only preyed upon by four-footed predators, but also crows and magpies. Foxes will readily consume clutches of duck eggs, but they will gobble up the mother duck, too, if they get the chance.

In Britain, a new predator for ducks to worry about is the North American mink, now firmly established throughout the country after escaping from fur farms. The mink is a voracious predator, and as its favoured habitat is along rivers or by the side of lakes, wildfowl feature prominently in its diet. Opinions vary as to how much impact the mink has had on nesting waterfowl, but its presence is certainly far from beneficial. Escaped mink in Iceland have certainly decimated populations of nesting waterfowl.

Ducks try to avoid four-footed predators by nesting on islands. For example, St Serf's island, on Loch Leven, is predator-free, and supports the densest population of nesting ducks anywhere in Britain. Up to 450 pairs of tufted ducks, as well as numerous other species, nest on this 39 acre (16 ha) island.

Huge numbers of European, Asian and North American ducks breed on the tundra of the Arctic. This annual influx of ducks offers a bonanza for the Arctic foxes. Though they mainly take eggs and ducklings, they will also kill adult birds if they can. However, their impact is much greater in years when lemming numbers are low, while it should also be remembered that the time of plenty is so brief that there is a limit to how many ducks and ducklings can be killed by the foxes. Foxes with full stomachs are quite content to doze in the summer sun, and do not spend all their time hunting.

Just as lions follow the migrating herds of wildebeest, so do predators like peregrine falcons and eagles follow the migratory

Mink

SPIKED

Pike have long been regarded as menace to breeding wildfowl, as they will pluck ducklings from the surface of the water. Large pike have even been seen to take adult ducks up to the size of a mandarin. However, experiments have shown that removing all the pike from a pond does not necessarily help the fortunes of the ducks. Fish and ducklings feed on the same invertebrates. Perch, rudd and chub will increase rapidly in numbers if pike are removed from a pond, and the explosion in fish numbers in a pike-less pond will mean less food for the ducklings. The latter are then much more likely to die from starvation. The balance of nature is very fine, and we alter it at our peril.

flocks of ducks. In the winter, estuaries or lakes with high numbers of ducks are also good places to look for avian predators. Peregrines kill by knocking their prey out of the sky, and they will take ducks as big as a mallard. Natural selection means that they usually attack the weakest or slowest-flying member of a flock. I remember once, during a bitter spell of weather, watching a peregrine attacking a mixed flock of 500 ducks on a French lake. Most of the lake was frozen, so the ducks were restricted to a small patch of open water. Each time the peregrine stooped at the ducks they all dived, but none made the mistake of trying to fly away. Eventually the falcon tired, and left the ducks in peace.

That same year in France, I was able to watch white-tailed eagles hunting the duck flocks. Their technique was much less spectacular than that of the peregrine, as they simply flew low over the ducks, making repeated passes until finally locating a weak or sick duck that hadn't the energy left to continue diving. On another occasion, on a Scottish estuary, I watched a great black-backed gull constantly chasing and harrying a female red-breasted merganser. The latter dived repeatedly, but each time she surfaced the gull was waiting for her, lunging at her once again. The chase went on for at least 10 minutes, and the merganser seemed doomed, as her dives were getting shorter and shorter. Then, suddenly and unexpectedly, the gull lost interest and flew away.

Behaviour

One of the most endearing features of ducks is their friendly and highly social behaviour. Most ducks clearly feel happiest when in company with others of their kind, and most species are found in flocks except during the breeding season. What is more, different species will often mix quite readily, with little in the way of arguing. However, not all ducks are quite as friendly. Adult steamer ducks usually live in pairs, never in flocks, and fierce and bloody territorial fights between rival steamers are not uncommon. However, juveniles and yearling birds will flock together. Another South American species, the crested duck, has also a reputation for being exceedingly aggressive, as does the bizarre Australian musk duck. All the shelducks are aggressive to others of their kind during the breeding season, though they will flock together during the rest of the year. Drake muscovies indulge in fierce fights, and so, too, do comb ducks.

Much of the early work on duck taxonomy (the relationships of species to each other) was based on studies of behaviour. The pioneer here was Konrad Lorenz. He studied a number of surface-feeding ducks, and, by comparing their behaviour patterns, was able to establish the probable evolutionary relationships of the birds. Today, analysis of the birds' DNA may give a more accurate idea of the relationship of the species, but studies of behaviour still hold a fascination for the biologist, and a source of pleasure for the birdwatcher.

Most of the shelduck are highly gregarious for much of the year, and especially when moulting. However, during the breeding season the drakes become extremely aggressive, not only to each other, but to other birds that enter into their territories. Confrontations between shelduck and avocets are a common sight at the RSPB's Minsmere Reserve, in Suffolk, in the spring.

Most ducks share the same basic behaviour. For example, the majority of species, when alarmed, will pump their heads up and down vigorously before taking flight. This is presumably a silent but highly visible warning to others members of the flock of the need to flee from a potential threat. It is the individual courtship displays of each species that particularly fascinate the biologists, who have given descriptive names (such as 'grunt whistle', 'cough', 'burp', 'neck-jerk' and 'head-throw') to the individual parts of the display. If you watch a courting group of mallard drakes you are sure to see them perform the grunt-whistle, as this is the most common mallard display. In this the drake raises his body up in the water, and at the same time arches his neck until his beak just touches the water. It is a simple, graceful movement which takes just a few seconds. He may follow this with what is known

Displaying mandarins

Two drake goldeneye displaying to a duck

as the 'head-up-tail-up' display, in which the head is raised, and the wings brought up behind the neck at the same time as the tail is extended. The mallard's courtship, like that of most ducks, is highly ritualised, and all the drakes in the group will go through exactly the same motions. Most of the mallard's close relatives perform the same or similar rituals. The display of the Laysan teal and the Hawaiian duck are virtually identical to the mallard, which explains why taxonomists have frequently regarded these birds as mere sub-species of the mallard.

For sheer visual delight, nothing beats watching a party of displaying mandarins. The drakes appear to puff themselves up, raising their crests, and fanning their wonderful, orange whiskers. At the same time they raise their orange 'sails', which really are remarkably enlarged inner secondary feathers. As the drakes paddle around, they indulge in what is known as the 'display shake', raising their breasts and at the same time pointing their beaks vertically at the water. This is followed by the ceremonious preening-behind-the-wing, a display that is usually directed at an individual duck. The drake delicately takes a tiny sip of water, and then with great ceremony raises one wing, which he carefully, but quickly, preens behind. Mere words fail to do justice to such actions, but as most wildfowl collections have mandarins, this is one display you can get out and see for yourself. Incidentally, mandarins tend to display most vigorously at dawn and dusk, and on dull days. It seems that they are aware that their dazzling plumage may well draw too much unwanted attention to themselves.

While the display of the drake mandarin is beautifully ordered and composed, like a perfectly choreographed dance, that of the drake goldeneye is real exhibitionist stuff. The most spectacular display is the head-throw-kick, in which the bird starts by pointing his beak vertically towards the sky, and flattening his body low on the water. Then he throws his head back rapidly, and kicks out vigorously with both feet at once, sending up a shower of spray. This is real rock and roll compared with the mandarin's ballet.

For comical appeal, the display of the drake ruddy duck takes a lot of beating. In what is known as the tail-flash, the drake cocks his tail vertically, showing off his white under-tail coverts. He clearly expects the female to find this rather sexy, as he will then swim deliberately in front of her, showing off the white feathers. This is a display never directed at other males, unlike bubbling, which is both elaborate and complex. He starts this by erecting his 'horns' and cocking his tail, and then suddenly beating his bill against his inflated neck, forcing air out from the feathers and causing bubbles to appear on the water. At the same time he produces a hollow tapping sound, which speeds up as the end of the display is approached. At the crescendo the drake cocks his tail even closer to his head, and lifts his folded wings for a moment, before deflating his air sac, and uttering a low belch.

In contrast to these avian exhibitionists, the whistling ducks hardly bother with displays at all, and nor does the muscovy. Most of the displays are a prelude to pair formation. Northern dabbling and diving ducks pair during the autumn, for displays begin as soon as the drakes are back in full plumage following the summer eclipse (see p. 72). Check a flock of wigeon in late winter and you will see the majority of the birds are paired, staying close to each other all the time. The only ducks which pair for life are those in which there is no eclipse plumage, such as the whistlers, and a number of other Southern Hemisphere birds. A few ducks, such as the muscovy, never pair at all. Most muscovy copulations take the form of rape, with the drake overpowering the much smaller duck.

It is the fact that most ducks have to find a new mate each year that has led to such intricate display patterns emerging, and also the evolution of such showy male plumages. If a drake is to pass his genes on to the next

Drake ruddy duck performing the bubbling display

WRONG END, MATE

generation, he has to be a success with the ducks, which is why so many drakes spend so much time displaying to their prospective mates. Furthermore, in most duck populations there are more drakes than ducks, so competition between the displaying drakes is invariably intense.

If you watch a group of mallard or teal in the early autumn, it may even appear that the drakes are more interested in showing off to each other than to the ducks. However, it is the presence of the ducks that stimulates the display in the first place. It is the duck who chooses her mate, presumably because he has impressed her with his courtship and the quality of his plumage. Once the two have paired, they will stay close to each other right through to the breeding season. Many ducks pair up early in the winter, so by December, most of the wigeon in a flock will already be in pairs. Though the pairs may have formed, much displaying continues, but the ducks, instead of being observers, now take part, encouraging their mates on with ritualised inciting behaviour.

Watch that same flock of wigeon and you will see that when the birds are grazing together, with the couples generally side by side, numerous arguments occur between the pairs. The duck will advance towards the pair she is quarrelling with, her head held low and neck stretched out. However, the attack is rarely, if ever, pressed home, and instead she will suddenly panic, and rush back to the security of her husband. But with him at her side she gets fresh courage, and will stand beside him and continue the argument. The duck of the opposing pair will mirror her behaviour, so you end up with two drakes standing erect with their heads up, and their wives growling at each other with heads low. The human observer is left wondering what was said to cause such a row. Usually nothing further happens, the argument is forgotten, and the birds get back to the serious business of grazing once again.

THEY BOTH WANTED
THE SAME BLADE OF GRASS

Mallard mating

MATING

Duck courtship is a public affair, but mating is rather more private. Copulation invariably takes place on the water, and the duck will demonstrate her willingness to mate by stretching her head forward and flattening her neck on the water. The drake then climbs on top of her, securing his precarious position by holding the feathers at the back of her neck with his beak. This hardly looks much fun for the duck, who usually ends up almost totally submerged, or with just her head out of the water.

With most birds, fertilisation is achieved by cloacal contact. (Unlike mammals, but as with reptiles, birds have a combined terminal opening of alimentary tract, excretory system and reproductive system, and this is called the cloaca or vent.) However, ducks are different in that the drake has an erectile penis, so that penetration is necessary for fertilisation to take place. So although mating (or 'treading') is a brief affair, duck copulations tend to take longer than those of most birds.

Once mating is complete, more ritualised behaviour usually takes place. Quite how intricate this is depends on the species. A drake mandarin dismounts immediately, and swims rapidly away, but performing what waterfowl biologists call 'turning-the-back-of-the-head' to the duck, with his tail slightly lifted. He doesn't turn to face her. The duck, unmoved by this, begins to bathe immediately.

Rather more flamboyant are the post-copulatory displays of members of the merganser family. The hooded merganser, for example, raises his crest fully during mating, and, once treading is completed, he retains hold of the duck's nape, and the two birds rotate together in nearly a complete circle. He then releases her, and 'steams' away with his crest still raised, before stopping to bathe.

Least romantic of the ducks is arguably the Australian musk duck. Though I have watched musk ducks in the wild, I have never seen them mating, but

according to observers who have, the drake does not have any special pre-copulatory behaviour, but simply displays with particular intensity when a female approaches closely. He then apparently throws a wing over her, pulls her underneath him and copulates. The unfortunate duck is completely sub-merged. Post copulatory display consists of the drake swimming away with his head under water, while the duck simply surfaces and flaps her wings. Musk ducks do not form pairs, a fact that seems hardly surprising with males that behave in such a way.

Ducks are unusually sexy birds, for mating between pairs may well occur throughout the winter, presumably strengthening the pair bond. This is in marked contrast to most species, which only mate shortly before egg laying. For example, Tim Birkhead, in his book *The Magpies*, estimates that each pair of magpies probably mates only three times for each clutch of eggs they lay. In contrast, a pair of mallard, or mandarins, will probably copulate scores of times.

It is important for the drake to escort the duck at all times, as other suit-ors are sure to be watching for the chance to slip in and mate with, or even

I'VE GOT A **HEAVY DATE** TONIGHT

rape, the duck. Rape is a particular problem for female mallard on urban ponds. The drakes greatly outnumber the ducks, a situation made worse when the majority of the ducks are away incubating their eggs. For the few remaining ducks on the pond, there are no secluded corners where they can loaf and avoid unwanted attention. Gangs of randy drake mallard may well pursue a single duck continually, even ignoring the fact that she has ducklings in tow. Such ducks often lose their ducklings, and end up with bald napes as a result of the drakes' unwanted attentions. It is not unusual for mallard ducks to be drowned under such circumstances. With many ducks, prolonged aerial chases are common in the spring, with a group of ducks pursuing a single duck across a marsh.

Of course, by the spring most ducks have long been paired, so the unpaired drakes become quite desperate in their pursuit of lone, unguarded ducks. It is an interesting fact that ducks are generally faithful to the area of their birth, returning to the same area to breed each year. In contrast, the drake follows his mate back to the latter's favoured nesting area. Thus a wigeon drake paired with an Icelandic hatched duck will return with her to Iceland; back on his English wintering grounds a few months later he may pair with a Siberian bird, and follow her back to Siberia the following spring.

Sub-species emerge when birds remain faithful to specific breeding areas. The white-fronted geese which breed in Greenland are easily recognisable by their orange-yellow bills, while birds from Russia have a fleshy-pink bill. Unlike the northern ducks, both sexes of geese remain faithful to the same breeding areas, so these regional, racial differences emerge. (There are four, possibly five, races of white-fronted goose.) In contrast, a pintail nesting in Siberia is identical to one nesting in Canada, and there is hardly any regional variation in any of the northern-nesting ducks. The reason for this lack of variety is due to the drake's tendency to follow his mate to her natal home, regardless of where he came from, thus mixing the blood lines continually.

The extravagant display of the drake red-breasted merganser

THE FASTEST HEAD-THROW IN THE WEST

Remarkably, two of the most similar of ducks, the greater and lesser scaup, have never been found to interbreed in the wild, despite a considerable overlap in their North American breeding range. Different habitat preferences apparently keep the two species apart, for wintering greater scaup prefer salt to freshwater, while lesser scaup stay on freshwater unless freezing weather pushes them to coastal lagoons and estuaries. The two species have been deliberately crossed in captivity, and produced fertile offspring. Wild lesser scaup have been reported to hybridise with canvasback, redhead and ringed-neck duck, so the lack of records of crossing with the greater scaup seems surprising. It seems likely that it does occur, but identifying the hybrids with certainty is almost impossible. Incidentally, the displays of the two species of scaup are very similar, and the main differences are the speed of the display (the lesser scaup performs the fastest head-throw of any duck) and the associated calls.

HYBRIDISATION

Ducks have such distinct plumages, and such intricate displays that there would seem to be little chance of hybrids occurring. Yet the ducks are responsible for the greatest number and variety of hybrids of any avian family. The mallard is alleged (though not proven) to have hybridised with no fewer than 45 other species of wildfowl, and even the Carolina wood duck has managed 26 mixed marriages. Most of these hybridisations have taken place in captivity, and are thus of less significance biologically. However, a substantial number of genuine wild hybrids occur in the wild each year, often confusing birdwatchers (and possibly their fellow ducks). According to one expert, wild hybrids occur at a ratio of one for every 60,000 individuals.

Duck hybrids tend to be fertile, and in captivity hybrids may mate with other hybrids, and produce the most extraordinary ducklings. In the wild, natural selection does not favour the hybrid bird, so the mixed blood is generally soon lost. Wild drake hybrids do not have either the right appearance, or the correct display, to attract a wife. However, the hybrid female may well be able to find a mate, but the alien blood will soon become diluted and of no significance to the population as a whole.

It is the distinctiveness of the drake's plumage, and the individuality of each species' display, that prevents hybridisation happening more often. Though many of the displays are similar in many ways – compare that of the mallard with the teal, for example – differences in the sequence, form or frequency help prevent cross matings between different species. Remember, also, that it is the duck that chooses her mate, not the other way round. A female gadwall and a female mallard may look very similar to the human eye, and if mate choice was left to the drake, one could understand him making mistakes. However, a drake mallard and a drake gadwall can hardly be confused with each other, so it is no wonder that wild ducks rarely choose the wrong husband. (Within the confines of captivity, rape is common, which explains why hybrids occur with such frequency. Also, if a duck in a collection lacks a mate of its own species, it is quite likely to find a substitute partner.)

It is not uncommon to find a marsh or lake with a considerable variety of different species nesting in close proximity to each other. Iceland's Lake Myvatn, for example, supports 16 species of nesting ducks, and some 10,000 pairs in all. Though many of the females may look similar to each other, all the males are very obviously different. It is a rule that the ducks with the widest ranges, and the greatest amount of sympathy with other closely related species, all tend to have the most elaborate displays and the most complex and distinctive male plumages. Classic examples are mallard, pintail and shoveler.

I HEAR HIS MUM USED TO PUT IT ABOUT A BIT

Plumed whistling duck

Identifying the parents of a hybrid duck can be extremely difficult, even for an expert. Though it is common for a hybrid to be an intermediate between its parents, it is not unusual for the bird to be unlike either parent, but resembling another species altogether. For example, drake hybrids resulting from a pairing between a teal and a shoveler, or a teal and a wigeon, invariably show a 'bridled' facial pattern resembling a Baikal teal. A cross between a tufted duck and a pochard is likely to look just like a lesser scaup, and such hybrids have confused and frustrated many birdwatchers. Today, most serious birders are well aware of the possibility of hybrids, so rare ducks are invariably carefully scrutinised to make sure they are what they appear to be.

NOISES

Quacking is one of the best-known of all bird sounds, but it is a curious fact that only a minority of ducks actually quack. Some whistle or growl, while others coo, squeak, bark, even yodel.

DID YOU HEAR A QUACK IN THERE?

What's more, ducks and drakes invariably have very different voices to each other. Ducks make noises for a variety of reasons, including courtship, warning of danger, and general communication. Quacking is largely the language of female surface-feeding ducks, of which the mallard is the best example. Drake mallard never quack, but have a much quieter, more nasal call. Watch a group of mallard for any length of time and you will be sure to hear this attractive sound.

Voice can be a reliable way to identify ducks. Flocks of wigeon identify themselves by the loud whistles of the drakes, and the harsh, growling calls of the ducks. The delightfully musical *krrit* call of a party of courting teal is unmistakable, as is the curious rattling of a drake garganey, which sounds like a fishing reel being wound in.

Some ducks take their name from the sounds they make. Whistling ducks do indeed whistle, while the North American name for the long-tailed duck – old squaw – reflects the fact that the male's yodelling song sounds just like an old squaw, nagging her husband. Many old country names similarly reflect the noises made by the birds in question. Wigeon have been called 'whistler', 'whim' and 'whewer' (the wigeon's whistle is a resounding *whee-oo*), while 'coo-doos' is a charming old name for the eider. There is no finer sound on a fine spring morning than that of a party of drake eiders, courting the ducks. The eiders really do coo, yet their cooing always seems to hold an element of surprise as they raise the second syllable.

Not all duck noises are made with the beak. Watch a displaying ruddy duck and you will hear a distinct drumming as he appears to beat his bill repeatedly in the water. In fact the bill is bouncing off inflated air sacs in his neck which produce the drumming sound (see p. 61). The whisper of duck

wings is distinctive, but certain species of whistling ducks have curiously shaped primary feathers which create a strange whistling sound when they fly. Such a sound may help members of the flocks stay in contact with each other when flying at night.

SAFETY IN NUMBERS

Joining together in large flocks helps duck survive, as, the bigger the flock, the more chance there is of a predator attacking another member of the group. There is also safety in numbers because there are more pairs of eyes looking for danger, and more chance that a predator will be spotted from afar. A lone duck is always much easier to approach closely than a flock. All the northern hemisphere ducks flock together in the winter, and individual flocks may include thousands of individual birds. Tropical species, such as whistling ducks, also join together in flocks. Only a minority of species – such as the New Zealand blue duck – never flock.

Drake garganey, a summer visitor to Europe and northern Asia

Like a duck to water

PLUMAGE

Look at a flock of mallard on a January day and it is a simple matter telling the drakes from the ducks. The drakes have bright, showy plumage: bottle-green heads contrasting with bright yellow bills, a burgundy breast, and predominantly grey body. The drake mallard is a real Beau Brummel of the duck world. In contrast, the females (or, more correctly, the ducks) have dowdy brown feathers. It is a classic example of what the biologists call 'sexual dimorphism'. However, inspect the same flock of mallard in mid-summer and you will have difficulty picking out the drakes, for at first glance it appears that there are none present. Look again and you will see that some of those 'ducks' are rather darker, their bills somewhat brighter, the breast feathers showing a hint of colour. They are not ducks at all, but drakes in what is called 'eclipse plumage'. Almost all the northern ducks have an eclipse plumage in the summer, when they moult their bright feathers, and replace them with a drab set that looks much more like those of their wives. The eclipse plumage makes them far less obvious, and in turn they tend to skulk in the reeds, well out of view. There is a reason for them becoming so shy, for

Shelduck on their summer moulting grounds on the Wadden See

MOULT MOVEMENTS

Special moult migrations are undertaken by a number of ducks. The best known is that of the shelduck. In mid-July, shelducks from all over north-west Europe move to the Heligoland Bight in the German Wadden See. Some 100,000 shelduck gather here for their annual get-together or summer holiday, and they stay on the Bight until well into September, or even longer. A similar, though much smaller, gathering takes place in Bridgwater Bay in Somerset at the same time. Here up to 3,000 ducks have been counted, though in recent years numbers have been considerably lower. When on the moulting grounds, the ducks undergo their annual moult, dropping their flight feathers and becoming flightless before growing their new feathers.

it is while they are in eclipse that they shed, and replace, their flight feathers. For a three-week period the drakes are completely flightless, until the new set of primaries is fully functioning. The ducks also drop their flight feathers at around the same time, usually when they have flightless ducklings in tow.

The length and timing of the eclipse varies from species to species. Mallard have one of the shortest periods, generally losing their bright plumage in early June, and looking bright and spruce again by early September. Other ducks are far more tardy about moulting back into full plumage. It is not until well into October that drake teal regain their breeding finery, while wigeon are usually a little later still. Slowest of the lot is the garganey. This beautiful little duck does not acquire his full breeding plumage until late January or early February, just before he leaves his wintering grounds in tropical Africa and India and starts his return journey north to Europe and Asia.

Southern hemisphere ducks are different than their northern counterparts in that they show far less sexual dimorphism – in other words it can be difficult to tell the boys from the girls. A female Chiloe wigeon, for example, looks like a duller version of her mate, and the same can be said for most of the South American, African and Australasian teal. Nor do these southern-ers have an eclipse plumage.

The plumage of the mallard varies little throughout its vast range, though plumage variations do occur where domesticated forms of mallard hybridise with genuine wild birds. Exceptionally dark, or pale, birds may then appear, while some may even be piebald. Such sports can confuse the inexperienced birdwatcher.

The shelduck is unusual in that it is the only duck that nests in Britain in which the sexes share identical plumage, though the duck is invariably some-what drabber than her mate. A simple way to tell the sexes apart is by looking at the beak: in the spring, the drake grows a large fleshy knob at the base of his bright red beak, but in the autumn this shrinks back in size and is less obvious.

Needless to say, there are always exceptions. The marbled teal of south-

SEE? CHICKENS CAN'T SWIM!

ern Europe and the Middle East is an oddity for a northern hemisphere duck in that the male and female look alike. Other excep-tions to the general rule include the torrent ducks of the Andes, in which the male is much brighter than the female, but he doesn't ever moult into an eclipse plum-age, though his beak does go a brighter shade of red in the breed-ing season.

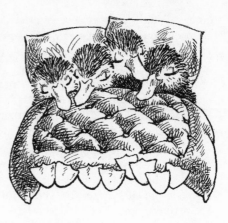

One feature common to all the ducks is waterproof plumage. The feathers gain their waterproofing by a coating of oil from the preen gland, hidden from view at the base of the tail. Watch a duck preen and you will see it will frequently touch this gland with its beak to ensure that its feathers remain fully proofed. Ducklings gain their waterproofing by contact with their mother's plumage. Ducklings reared under a foster hen lack this protection, so can become wet and waterlogged when they first attempt to swim.

Underneath the top feathers are the soft, downy feathers which insulate the bird from the cold. Swimming on icy water would be an unpleasant experience without this protection. As you would expect, ducks that live in cold regions carry much more down than tropical species.

Man long ago discovered the value of duck down as a filling for quilts, and found that the very best down came from the eider duck. Eiderdown is the lightest, softest and most elastic of all duck down. In Iceland, eider ducks have been 'farmed' for centuries. The nesting ducks are supplied with an ample choice of nest sites, and are protected from predators. The first supply of down is taken from the nest shortly after incubation has started. This the mother duck replaces over the next few days. Then, when the ducklings have hatched and the nest is abandoned, the remaining down is collected. Today, bed quilts are generally known as 'eiderdowns', regardless of whether they are filled with synthetic fibres, ordinary duck down or the real thing. The word 'duvet' comes from the French name for an eider, *eider à duvet*.

Quite how many feathers a duck has depends on the species, and the time of the year. Small ducks, such as teal, have around 11,500, but larger ducks may have several thousand more.

SWIMMING AND DIVING

Not every duck can fly, but every one can swim. All the ducks have webbed feet, which give them the propulsion required to paddle along in the water. As a general rule, the larger a duck's feet in proportion to its body, the more time it spends swimming. Some of the surface-feeding ducks, such as teal and even mallard, spend relatively little time swimming, as they find their food in shallow, puddled ground where the water is often not deep enough to swim in. Other groups, such as the wood ducks and shelduck, do most of their foraging on dry land. In contrast, others rarely land. The stifftails, for example, spend almost all their time on water, only coming ashore to lay their eggs.

The mallard is the classic example of a surface-feeding duck. It feeds on or around the surface of the water, usually by dabbling or upending while swimming, but will just as readily forage on dry land. It can dive well, but rarely dives for food. However, I have watched mallard diving for acorns in the autumn, and this is apparently relatively common behaviour. The diet is enormously varied, and though it is principally a vegetarian, eating grains, seeds and water plants, it has been recorded consuming a huge variety of other foods, ranging from locusts to tadpoles. Urban mallard show a great liking for bread, with no particular preference for white or brown.

While the surface-feeding ducks rarely dive for their food, diving ducks do so all the time. They are better adapted for diving than the surface-feeders, with their legs set farther back on their bodies. When they are underwater, they use their feet for propulsion. Diving is hard work, as the bird has to overcome its natural buoyancy to remain submerged for any length of time.

Watch a diving duck feeding and you will notice that before each dive, it draws its feathers in tight to the body, thus reducing to a minimum the trapped air in the plumage. In order to dive as deeply as possible, ducks such as pochards and tufted ducks really plunge into the water. However, watch an eider or scoter undertake the same manoeuvre and you will see it open its wings as it starts the dive. These sea ducks use their wings as well as their feet when diving, and this allows them to dive to much greater depths, and stay under for longer. In contrast, stifftail ducks simply seem to breathe in and sink below the surface of the water, not leaving as much as a ripple behind. This is a trait they share with the grebes.

It is obviously difficult to discover how deep ducks dive, but the champion appears to be the long-tailed duck, as it has been recorded diving to

Mallard upending

depths of as much as 150 metres (500 feet) in the Great Lakes of North America. Scoters and eiders frequently dive to depths of 30 metres (100 feet) or more, while the majority of dives undertaken by tufted ducks and pochard are certainly much shallower. The deeper the dive the longer the bird stays under: most freshwater diving ducks remain under the surface for less than a half a minute, but if you put a stopwatch on a feeding eider you will discover that it often stays under for up to two minutes.

GOING UNDER

Studies of pochard have shown that they spend about 29% of their day feeding. Most of their dives go no deeper than 2.5 metres (10 feet), and the average length of a dive is about 20 seconds. Drakes apparently dive deeper than ducks, and the latter prefer to feed in shallower areas. Tufted ducks tend to dive a little deeper than pochard, and the drakes tend to remain underwater slightly longer than the ducks.

Feeding

VEGETARIAN OR CARNIVORE?

Contrary to popular opinion, only a minority of ducks eat fish. The great majority of surface-feeding ducks are omnivorous, living mainly on vegetable matter, but taking meat, such as insects and tadpoles, when they get the chance. Some of the surface feeders have specially adapted beaks that restrict the food they eat. The shoveler is a classic example. All four species of shoveler have spatulate bills that allow them to filter water, sucking it in as they swim along, then expelling it out again at the sides. As they do this, so they draw off the food particles they are looking for, such as plankton, caddis flies, tadpoles, spiders, crustaceans, insect larvae and seeds. The beak is specially adapted for this with edges that have long, comb-like lamellae (fine, hair-like structures lining the beak) that help trap the food. Shovelers are gregarious feeders, and it is usual to see groups of five or six birds swimming together, with heads and necks stretched forward, and beaks partly submerged. The birds at the back do best, as each bird feeds in the water disturbed by the duck ahead. All the shovelers prefer to feed in shallow, freshwater marshes, but they can be found on estuaries, and often rest in flocks on the sea.

Because of the high proportion of animal matter in the diet, the flesh of the shoveler makes poor eating. They are sometimes known as the neighbour's mallard in the USA, as successful duck hunters keep the mallard they have shot, but give away the inedible shovelers to their neighbours. Similarly, in Australia the shoveler is sometimes known as the stinker, due to the nasty smell of a roasting bird.

Like the shoveler, the pink-eared duck also has a big, shovel-shaped beak. What makes it even more unusual is the fleshy flap on the sides of the upper mandible, rather like those of the blue duck. Such adaptations to the bill no doubt help the pink-eared when feeding: it is also a filter feeder, swimming in small groups and sifting the water with beak almost totally immersed. In both appearance and behaviour it resembles the shoveler, but the two are not related, and the fact they look so similar is a classic case of what is known as convergent evolution. (The two have evolved to fill a similar ecological niche.) Because of its specialised feeding habits, you would expect the pink-eared to be rare, but it is both numerous and widespread in Australia.

It is not uncommon to find vegetarian and animal-eating ducks side by side on the same lake or pond. Visit any British gravel pit or reservoir in the winter and you are sure to see a mixed flock of tufted ducks and pochard. In their general shape they look very similar, with rounded bodies and short tails that float on, or close to, the water. They both feed by diving, making

European shovelers have specialised bills for filter feeding

little jumps out of the water before plunging head-first under. Despite their similarities, the two species are not competing directly with each other. Pochard are principally vegetarian, while the more omnivorous tufted ducks are seeking molluscs, crustaceans and insects. There is, of course, some overlap in their diets, but it does mean that the two species can live happily side by side.

The best-known of the fish-eating ducks are the sawbills – the mergansers. The word 'sawbill' is an apt description of these ducks' beaks, which are long, thin and with a serrated edge. Such a beak is perfectly adapted for catching fast-swimming and slippery fish, which form the bulk of their diet. All the mergansers dive for their prey, and all are highly efficient underwater swimmers. However, in shallow water it is not unusual to watch a merganser paddling along with its head underwater as it forages for fish fry. Most of the fish caught by mergansers are fairly small, and all will be swallowed head-first in order to ensure that the spines and fins do not catch in the throat. There are, however, records of mergansers choking to death as a result of trying to swallow fish too big to slide down their gullets. Mergansers will certainly take other animal food that is available: goosanders (the largest of the family) have been recorded killing and eating ducklings, as well as taking frogs, snakes and small mammals such as shrews.

One of the most specialist insectivorous ducks is the New Zealand blue duck. It lives on fast-flowing mountain rivers in New Zealand (on both North and South Island), and is not really blue, but a shade of slate-grey. Both sexes look alike. If you get close to a blue duck you will see that it has a curious pale bill, with flaps of skin towards the tip. These presumably help it when it is foraging for invertebrates. The rivers it lives in are generally turbulent but shallow, so it feeds more by swimming, with head and neck submerged, than by diving.

HE DABBLES IN THE STOCK MARKET

The South American crested duck is generally regarded as the world's most carnivorous duck. It feeds in a shelduck-like way, foraging on foot in the shallows, or swimming and upending in deeper water, looking for molluscs and similar food. It has a reputation for consuming anything of animal origin it encounters, and is often found in the vicinity of slaughter houses where it will feast on floating offal. Australia can also boast a meat-eating duck: the curious musk duck. This is one of the strangest of all the waterfowl, as well as one of the ugliest. Musk ducks are carnivorous, eating anything from fish to frogs, and even ducklings. One highly unusual trait is that the female feeds the ducklings, something no other species of waterfowl does, except for the Australian magpie goose.

SALT OR FRESHWATER?

Some ducks rarely ever venture away from freshwater, while others spend nearly all their lives on salt water. Many, however, divide their time between the two. Take the mallard as an example. Town parks may be a favourite habitat, but mallard are equally at home on the Arctic tundra, or sub-tropical pools, and are not too fussy about the water they swim on. Freshwater may be preferred, but they will also frequent brackish estuaries and lagoons, and can often be found on the sea, though they seldom move far from the sight of land.

SAWBILL AND SALMON

The favoured food of both the red-breasted merganser and the goosander are game fish. Studies of the goosander in Britain have shown that as much as 80% of the diet is made up of young salmon and trout. This makes them highly unpopular with fishery managers, who believe that these ducks are the reason for dwindling stocks. As a result they have been widely persecuted on their breeding grounds in both North America and Europe. In Britain, both sawbill ducks are protected under the Wildlife and Countryside Act, and can only be shot legally under licence. For a licence to be granted, evidence of 'serious damage' to fisheries is required. Considerable numbers of nesting sawbills have been shot under licence (and no doubt many more without a licence). However, there is no evidence that predation by these ducks of young fish has any impact on the number of fish that mature and are available for anglers to catch. Shooting of red-breasted mergansers in Scotland and Ireland has led to a decline in numbers of nesting birds in many areas, while the continued expansion of the goosander's British breeding range is remarkable in view of the continuing persecution.

Harlequins spend the summer on freshwater, but winter at sea

In Britain, the scaup is almost exclusively a sea duck, and is rarely found on freshwater. Molluscs are its principal winter food, but the British wintering flocks are usually concentrated around such unnatural food sources as sewage outflows and distillery discharges. In the summer, scaup forsake the sea, and breed by freshwater lakes and ponds on the Arctic tundra. Similarly, common scoters spend much of the year at sea, though generally not far offshore, where they feed by diving for shellfish. They float buoyantly, and rarely come ashore even to rest. If you see a scoter on a beach, then it is likely to be ill. Because of their maritime lifestyle, scoters are highly vulnerable to oiling. In the breeding season they leave the sea, and move inland to nest close to freshwater lakes. Unlike the scoters and eiders, goldeneye are much more flexible in their choice of habitat. In the winter many feed in estuaries and coastal waters, but others move inland to freshwater lakes and reservoirs.

The majority of Cape teal never see the sea, but many spend much of their lives on salt waters, for this little African duck has a genuine liking for saline water. I have watched Cape teal on Kenya's Lake Nakuru, where they are usually present in small numbers, and they can often be found on other soda lakes of the Rift Valley.

Steamer ducks are among the most maritime of all the wildfowl, spending almost all their lives on salt water. However, the closely related flying steamers show a liking for freshwater, and, though they often occur on the sea, they can also be found well inland. In Patagonia, I have encountered them on lakes in the foothills of the Andes, at least 150 miles from the sea.

Few ducks are more specialised than the harlequin, which spends its summers on fast-flowing rivers and streams. However, many of these streams freeze in the winter, forcing the harlequins on to the sea. In contrast, the South American torrent duck, another fast-water specialist, remains on its mountain rivers throughout the year.

For ducks that spend all or most of their time at sea, drinking freshwater is clearly an impossibility. Thus the birds will readily drink salt water. As the avian kidney has only a limited ability to excrete salt, the birds rid themselves of the excess salt through the nasal salt glands. This is a cunning way of dealing with a tricky problem. Quite how they manage such a complicated physiological process has long fascinated biologists, who have done most of their research work with mallard. The mallard was chosen because it is such an easy bird to handle, and also because its nasal salt glands secrete readily when the bird is given excess salt. Some ducks, such as steamers, may never drink freshwater throughout their lives. However, most ducks prefer to drink freshwater rather than salt if given the choice. Cape teal, for example, may occur on the salt lakes of the Rift Valley in East Africa, but they can often be found feeding, drinking and bathing where the freshwater streams flow into the lakes.

Aliens and rarities

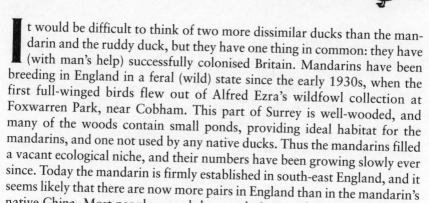

It would be difficult to think of two more dissimilar ducks than the mandarin and the ruddy duck, but they have one thing in common: they have (with man's help) successfully colonised Britain. Mandarins have been breeding in England in a feral (wild) state since the early 1930s, when the first full-winged birds flew out of Alfred Ezra's wildfowl collection at Foxwarren Park, near Cobham. This part of Surrey is well-wooded, and many of the woods contain small ponds, providing ideal habitat for the mandarins, and one not used by any native ducks. Thus the mandarins filled a vacant ecological niche, and their numbers have been growing slowly ever since. Today the mandarin is firmly established in south-east England, and it seems likely that there are now more pairs in England than in the mandarin's native China. Most people regard the mandarin as a charming, though exotic, addition to the countryside.

Until recently, the same view was held about the ruddy duck. Britain's burgeoning ruddy duck population is descended from a few birds imported by the Wildfowl Trust after the Second World War. The ruddies settled in at Slimbridge, and soon started breeding at their new home. Ruddy ducks are secretive nesting birds, so a few ruddy ducklings were hatched and reared by their mothers, and escaped pinioning. These full-winged birds eventually left Slimbridge, moving to nearby gravel pits, and then on to Chew Valley Lake in Somerset, where they bred for the first time in the early 1960s. Like the mandarin, the ruddy duck filled a vacant niche, for there is no similar stifftail in northern Europe. Slowly but surely numbers started to grow, and new areas were colonised by the ruddies. The meres of Shropshire proved particularly popular, and by the end of the 1980s Britain's ruddy duck population had reached an estimated 4,000 birds.

It is easy to see why the ruddy ducks were so successful, for they found ideal habitat, and favourable weather conditions not dissimilar to those in their native North America. What is more, they were not molested, for ruddy ducks are reluctant fliers, so are not a sporting quarry. Birdwatchers welcomed these entertaining little ducks, and members of the West Midland Bird Club even adopted the ruddy as their logo.

However, in the early '90s the ruddy duck suddenly fell from grace. Spanish ornithologists reported that invading male ruddy ducks had arrived on lakes in Andalucia inhabited by the rare and endangered white-headed duck, a closely related stifftail. What was more, the aggressive drake ruddies were seducing, even raping, the female white-headed ducks, and hybrids were appearing as a result. As the Spanish had spent a great deal of time, money and effort on restoring the white-headed duck population, they were not too

North American ruddy ducks are now well established in Britain

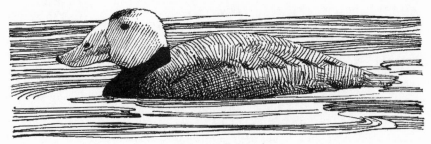

White-headed duck

pleased. An urgent request was sent to Britain, asking that the ruddy ducks should be controlled, and thus stopped from heading for Spain, and indulging in such lager-lout behaviour.

This threw the British ornithological hierarchy into turmoil. It was soon agreed by English Nature, the RSPB and the Wildfowl and Wetlands Trust that control was needed, though no-one knew how to go about it. At the same time, many birdwatchers disagreed with the decision to try and wipe out the ruddies, and refused to help those who wanted them eradicated. However, experiments in ruddy duck control started to take place, with attempts to shoot the unfortunate birds, as well as find, and destroy, their nests. These experiments met with some success, though it seems unlikely that the ruddy duck will ever be eradicated from Britain. Like those other unloved North American immigrants, the mink, grey squirrel and Canada goose, it appears to be here to stay. The best the anti-ruddy ducks campaigners can hope for is a control on numbers, thus stopping any further expansion. Ruddy ducks are already nesting in France and Holland, so the moves being taken in England are probably too late already.

Disasters with alien species are nothing new. Mallard have been released in numerous countries, almost always as a sporting bird. Many of these introductions failed, but others succeeded, invariably with unforeseen consequences. In New Zealand, the various acclimatisation societies (whose aim was to introduce as many British birds to New Zealand as possible) released hundreds of mallard in the early 1900s. In 1917, the first hybrids

INTRODUCTION OF THE RUDDY DUCK

ESCAPES OR MIGRANTS

Hooded mergansers have been recorded regularly in Britain in recent years, but the majority of these birds are likely to have escaped from captivity, for this interesting and good-looking bird has become popular in wildfowl collections where they are now bred in some numbers. Most of the birds recorded in Britain have been tame and approachable, suggesting a captive origin. However, hooded mergansers are still expensive ducks to buy, so it is unlikely that collections are deliberately letting their birds escape, and the odd genuine migrant from North America might reach our shores.

---

between mallard and the native New Zealand grey duck were shot. It was soon discovered that the two species could interbreed freely, producing fertile offspring. What was more, the mallard proved to be more adaptable than the greys, out-competing the natives for food, laying more eggs and raising more ducklings. Today the mallard is the dominant duck in New Zealand, especially in the settled areas and on lowland farms.

Mallard were also introduced into Australia, where again they hybridised with the native black duck. However, here they have been less successful, perhaps because they have abandoned their migratory instincts, which makes them less able to cope with the changeable Australian climate. Mallard remain a familiar sight on ponds in many city parks, particularly around Sydney, but it seems unlikely that they will ever colonise the continent. Mallard have also been released in South Africa, where they have hybridised with the native yellow-billed duck. Fortunately, they do not seem to have become established.

THREATENED DUCKS

Three ducks have been exterminated in the last 150 years: how many will join them in the next 150? According to BirdLife International, no fewer than 19 species are regarded as globally threatened. (Somewhat optimistically, since they are probably already extinct, BirdLife lists additionally the crested shelduck and pink-headed duck in the globally threatened list.) The majority of these threatened species have declined due to a combination of loss of habitat (chiefly drainage of their wetland habitats) and over-hunting. These are certainly the principal reasons for the black-billed (West Indian) whistling duck's massive decline. Though this species is widely distributed in the West Indies, its status is precarious. There are no official estimates of its total population. In contrast, the most recent counts of the Australian freckled duck estimate its population at rather fewer than 20,000 birds. Some

---

PASSPORTS FOR POCHARDS

Often forgotten, or even overlooked, is the tiny breeding population of red-crested pochards in Britain, centred on the Cotswold Water Park. They nested here for the first time in 1975, and the populations has grown steadily ever since. However, it still remains very small. No-one knows where these ducks came from originally, but they were almost certainly escapees from a wildfowl collection, for red-crested pochards are popular in captivity, where they breed freely. Vagrant red-crested pochards occur regularly in Britain, so the Cotswold birds can almost be considered a natural addition to our avifuana, and qualify for a British passport.

75% of the wetlands on the Perth coastal plain, one of the most important breeding areas, have been drained or significantly altered. Though the freckled duck is protected by law, numbers still get shot by hunters who are unable to identify their quarry correctly before pulling the trigger.

Hunting has always been a problem for the white-headed duck. In the late '60s I watched white-headed ducks being shot during a coot shoot on a lagoon in Andalucia in southern Spain. The white-headed duck was already rare in Spain then, but by the end of the '70s its future looked even more doubtful. Fortunately its plight was recognised in time, and by the mid '90s

The bizarre spectacled eider, a mystery bird

Pacific black duck

the population had climbed back to a more satisfactory 500 birds. Now protected, its future is imperilled more by invading ruddy ducks than hunters. (See Aliens, p. 85) Elsewhere in its wide range, numbers have tumbled, and in many countries where it once bred it no longer occurs.

My favourite of the shelduck tribe is also the smallest and the rarest. To see the radjah shelduck you need to travel to tropical Australia, though this distinctive species is also widespread in New Guinea. I saw my first radjahs on a marsh not far from Townsville, in Queensland, but it was not until I visited Darwin, some years later, that I really got to know this bird. This is one of the few places where it is quite common, even on lakes in the town parks. Unlike its wary southern cousin, the Australian shelduck, the radjah is quite tame and reluctant to fly. This has often been its undoing, for this species has been hunted heavily, despite its flesh making poor eating. This has made it the rarest of its tribe, its future the least certain.

With the Arctic-nesting eiders, one would expect few problems, but sadly this is not the case. Two species are regarded as threatened: Steller's eider and the spectacled eider. Steller's is the smallest of the eiders, and is named after Georg Wilhelm Steller, the 18th-century Arctic explorer and naturalist. Steller's eider breeds principally along the Arctic coasts of eastern Siberia to coastal Alaska, but occasionally nests elsewhere in the Arctic, and has even been recorded doing so in Norway. Norway's Varanger Fjord is the most reliable site in Europe to see this high Arctic species, as small numbers are usually present here throughout the year. Numbers of Steller's eiders have dropped alarmingly in recent years, though not as badly as the spectacled eider.

The spectacled eider is something of a mystery bird, for though we know where it breeds – in eastern Siberia and north and west Alaska – its wintering grounds have never been discovered. It seems most likely that the flocks spend their winters along the southern edge of the pack ice in the Bering Sea. Vagrants have occasionally been recorded thousands of miles from the known range, with records from northern Norway and western Siberia, but this is the only eider that has never been recorded in British waters. Few ducks are as bizarre in their plumage as the aptly named spectacled eider. Some people regard the spectacled eider as ugly, while others claim it to be one of the most beautiful of the world's waterfowl. It is a very rare bird in duck collections, so if you want to form your own opinion on the appearance of this strange duck, then the Yukon-Kuskokwim delta of Alaska is the place to go. In the mid-70s its world population was thought to be as high as 400,000 individuals. Since then there has been a huge decline, perhaps by as much as 90%, but no-one knows why. Locating the spectacled eider's wintering grounds may be the key to its future.

Another duck whose numbers have crashed alarmingly is the delightful Baikal teal, and in many areas where it was once an abundant winter visitor (such as Japan) it is now very uncommon. Only in South Korea are wintering numbers still counted in thousands. It appears that this duck has been unable to withstand the intense hunting pressure to which it has been subjected in recent years. Its habit of gathering in large, dense flocks made it particularly vulnerable to both netting and shooting, while there are also records of hunters taking large numbers by baiting them with poisoned grain. If present declines continue, the Baikal teal could well be critically endangered in the near future.

Marbled teal have probably never been an abundant species. Birds of shallow, eutrophic lakes (freshwater lakes rich in nutrients), their range extends from southern Spain and Morocco in the west to China in the east. Today their range is very fragmented, and they have been lost from many areas where they once occurred. Their numbers are subject to fluctuation, and in the marismas of the Coto Doñana in southern Spain numbers have increased recently, after a long decline. However, the total world population is put at a mere 33,000 birds, and the destruction of the marshes in southern Iraq is probably the greatest threat to the species.

Another European-nesting duck in serious trouble is the ferruginous duck. Unlike most diving ducks, the ferruginous favours shallow pools and marshes with lots of vegetation both in the water and on the shoreline. It is no doubt drainage of areas like these that have led to a huge drop in numbers of this species. Its range is vast, extending from Spain and Morocco, through much of central and eastern Europe across to India, Mongolia and China. Latest estimates put the population at a mere 75,000 birds, though as recently as 1970 there were thought to be 140,000 nesting pairs in the former USSR.

Baer's pochard is a little-known species which resembles the ferruginous duck in both appearance and choice of habitat. Its breeding range extends through eastern Russia and north-east China to North Korea, while it winters as far south as north-east India, Bangladesh and Hong Kong. Once described as 'extremely abundant', it is no longer, and the total population is probably below 10,000 birds.

Marbled teal, one of the most endangered of the world's ducks

Relatively few species of ducks live in tropical rainforests, so the destruction of these forests has had little impact on ducks in general. However, one species has suffered: the white-winged wood duck. Originally found over a wide area of south-east Asia, extending from north-east India all the way to Indonesia, it has now disappeared from most of its former haunts. Large and good to eat, it has always been hunted, but deforestation of the lowlands has destroyed its habitat and sent numbers plummeting. The world population may well be below 500 birds, making this one of the most endangered of ducks. A captive-breeding programme is being used to supplement wild stocks.

Another rainforest duck is the Brazilian merganser. Its range extends from south-central Brazil to eastern Paraguay and northern Argentina, where it favours shallow, fast-flowing rivers. Once thought to be extinct, it was rediscovered in 1948. However, it remains critically endangered (chiefly because of deforestation), and this is one species that will be lucky to survive long into the 21st century. It occurs in extremely low numbers in just a few widely separated localities.

Another South American duck in trouble is the southern pochard. This rather large, dark diving duck is locally quite common, even abundant, in East and Southern Africa. However, in South America it is now extremely rare. The lack of recent records suggest that this duck may be seriously endangered here, though it fails to get a mention in *The Threatened Birds of the Americas*, published by ICBP/IUCN in 1992.

The scaly-sided merganser occurs on the opposite side of the globe, in mountainous areas of eastern Russia, North Korea and north-east China. Here the total population is estimated at no more than 4,000 birds, and is still declining. Logging, hunting, water pollution, silting of shallows by industrial installations and river traffic are all hastening its decline.

Island birds are always vulnerable, and none more so than the Laysan teal, which occurs exclusively on the tiny Pacific island of Laysan. Numbers this century have fluctuated between one and 500, but this is one species that is well represented in wildfowl collections around the world. The same cannot be said of the Madagascar teal, an endemic to this Indian Ocean island. However, a captive breeding programme has been started as insurance against the wild population falling any further. How many survive in the wild is unknown, but the total is probably under 1,000, and may be considerably less. The Madagascar teal has been much persecuted in the past. Even rarer than the teal is the Madagascar pochard. There were only a scattering of records of this bird during the last 50 years, but in August 1991 a single male was captured alive. Intensive searches have followed since, but no more birds have been seen. If it is not already extinct, then this is the world's most critically endangered duck. Jean Delacour collected a number of Madagascar pochard in the 1920s, and brought them back to Europe where they bred successfully. Sadly, the Second World War wiped this captive population out.

Hunting has probably never been a major problem for the blue duck, which occurs on fast-flowing mountain rivers in both North and South Island, New Zealand. Since European settlement its range has contracted up from the lowlands, but even in the mountains its survival is now threatened by hydro-electric schemes, pollution and deforestation. The total population is estimated at between 2,000 and 4,000 birds, which means it almost certainly outnumbers another New Zealand endemic, the brown teal. Excessive shooting, wetland drainage and the introduction of mammalian predators have all played their part in the disappearance of this teal, which is now found in greatest numbers (c 1,400) on Great Barrier Island. In October 1987 I saw a pair on Kapiti Island, where they are believed to be resident but are only rarely recorded. Ten captive-bred pairs had been released on Kapiti several years before, and the birds I saw were probably their progeny. Brown teal from the mainland of New Zealand can fly, but the races from the Auckland Islands and Campbell Island are flightless. Ironically, the teal has died out on both Auckland Island itself, and Campbell Island, but survives on outlying islands where it is safe from introduced predators such as black rats and cats.

Lastly, Salvadori's teal is widely distributed on alpine lakes and fast-flowing rocky streams in the mountains of New Guinea. One would have thought it was safe here, especially as large areas of suitable habitat remain, but it is having to contend with pollution from copper and gold mines, increased hunting pressure, and also competition for its food from trout which have been introduced to rivers within its range.

A pair of crested shelduck, a fabled bird that is probably extinct

---

CAPTIVE BREEDING

Most species of ducks will breed readily in captivity, so maintaining captive breeding stocks of endangered birds is vitally important. The Wildfowl and Wetlands Trust has bred many rare ducks, and helped build up the captive populations of many endangered species. Some, such as the white-winged wood duck, have been used for re-introduction programmes. However, re-introducing captive birds is never easy, as a great deal of work must be done before birds are released to ensure that they do not die out again. When their extinction is related to loss of habitat this can be difficult. However, where ducks have been wiped out by over-hunting there is a good chance of re-introductions succeeding, as long as protection is well enforced.

EXTINCT DUCKS

Every few years, reports come from the remote hill country of Burma that someone has seen a pink-headed duck. Whether they have done so seems highly unlikely, as the last positive sightings of this extraordinary looking duck, with its black plumage and pink head, were back in 1935. Always rare, this duck finally disappeared, for unknown reasons, though over-hunting and the conversion of its habitat into agricultural land seem the most likely reasons. It is thought that the last known birds survived in Jean Delacour's collection at Clères, in Normandy, until the outbreak of war in 1939. These individuals had been imported from Calcutta in 1929. Sadly, they never bred in captivity. Jean Delacour's notes on their general habits, in Volume two of *The Waterfowl of the World*, conjures up an image of a long-lost world: 'They used to be fairly numerous a hundred years ago in the Duars of Eastern Bengal and now and then came up when lines of elephants were employed to beat through thick grass or jungle in tiger hunts.'

Even more mysterious than the pink-headed duck is the crested shelduck. Like the pink-headed duck, the crested shelduck has a striking appearance, and is easy to identify, while it features in ancient Japanese and Chinese art. Its range extended through eastern Russia, North and South Korea and into Japan, though it must always have been rare. There have been a number of confirmed sightings during the last 40 years, including three at Vladivostock in May 1964, six in North Korea in March 1971, and two in eastern Russia in March 1985. However, though much of its range is little explored ornithologically, the chances of a viable population surviving must be remote.

For the third species of duck – the Auckland Islands merganser – to have become extinct in the 20th century, there is no hope of an unknown

population being discovered. Both sexes of this duck resembled a female red-breasted merganser. The Auckland Islands merganser was first collected and described in 1840. The last birds were shot in 1902, and eventually ended up in the British Museum. It seems likely that overhunting, plus the impact of introduced mammalian predators, sealed the fate of this interesting bird. This small population of mergansers in the Aukland Islands seemed improbable, as it was so isolated from any other mergansers. However, research has shown that a similar merganser lived on South and Stewart Islands, New Zealand, until relatively recently.

The Auckland Islands merganser just survived into the 20th century, but the Labrador duck failed to do so, the last bird being taken near Long Island, on the east coast of the USA, in October 1875. This handsome sea duck was always rare, and its final disappearance remains a mystery. However, it was obviously a highly specialised bird, and it seems likely that it was unable to cope with even the slightest changes in its environment.

Man and duck

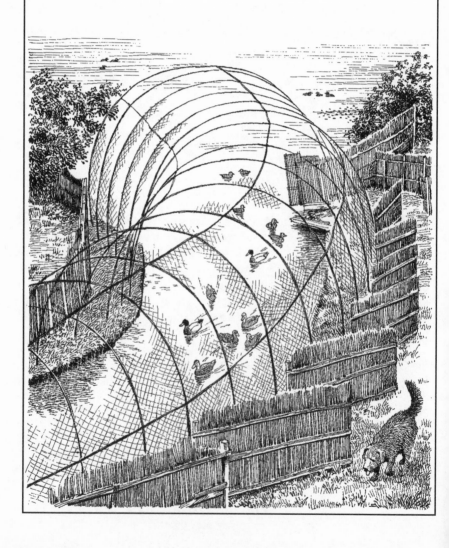

DOMESTIC DUCKS

Nobody knows when man (and woman) first domesticated the duck, but it was certainly many centuries ago. However, though we are aware that the Egyptians domesticated the goose, it appears that they ignored the duck. Most historians believe that it was the Romans who first kept mallard in captivity, while the Malays in Asia did likewise. It was hardly surprising that the mallard was domesticated, for this successful species has long lived in close proximity to man, and it is by far the most adaptable of all the ducks.

Only one other species of duck has ever been domesticated: the muscovy. While the Romans were busy with their tame mallard, it seems likely that in the rainforests of South America, the Indians were already keeping muscovy ducks. The muscovy is a common inhabitant of the tropical forests of Central and South America. The Indians like pet animals, and the first tame muscovies were probably kept as pets, valued not only for their companionship, but also their ability to eat bugs in and around the houses. Most domesticated muscovy can still fly, despite their bulk. In contrast, domesticated forms of mallard lost their flying ability long ago.

Man is a great manipulator, and it was by selective breeding of the mallard that all the breeds we know today slowly evolved. At least 20 breeds are recognised in Britain, and there are many more in south and east Asia, where some 75% of the world's domestic ducks are kept. The Chinese have always regarded ducks as superior birds to chickens, both as producers of meat and eggs.

Many modern breeds are quite extraordinary in their appearance. Some, like the Rouen, still retain a similar plumage to the wild ancestors, but have become so gross they weigh four times as much. Perhaps the most unusual birds to look at are the Indian runners, which stand strikingly upright. This curious breed evolved in the rice paddies of Asia hundreds of years ago. The birds were marched every morning to the paddies by their shepherd, or rather duckherd, where they would spend the day foraging for snails and

LEFT *A traditional duck decoy, once a regular source of ducks for the table*
RIGHT *Indian runner*

*Muscovy, a species that was first domesticated in South America
many centuries ago*

seeds. In the evening they would be marched back home to roost, and lay
eggs. Selective breeding ensured that the runners were prodigious layers of
eggs, and that the ducks rarely went broody. This meant that the ducklings
had to be hatched and reared under foster mothers – usually chickens. Today, runners are still marched daily to the paddies in many parts of Asia, just
as they have been for centuries.

Change of colour is one of the most obvious signs of domestication, and
domesticated mallard come in a wide variety of different plumages, of which
white is the most common. The classic white duck is the Aylesbury, but the
smaller Pekin is also white, and is the world's most popular domestic duck. As
its name suggests, it origins are Chinese. Some domestic breeds take their name
from their colour. Examples are the Khaki Campbell (khaki is a Hindustani

word for the colour of dust, but the Dust Campbell hardly has the same ring about it), and the Black East Indian. The latter's plumage may look black from a distance, but close to it appears shot with purple and green.

Not all domestic ducks were developed for their eggs or meat. Call ducks were originally bred to lure their wild relations into decoys, or traps. Small birds were preferred, as they ate less, while the noisiest individuals were also the most popular. Modern call ducks are both small and noisy, and, though they are usually white, they also come in shades of buff, as well as original mallard. They are an exception among domestic ducks in that they retain their powers of flight. Today, call ducks are popular as ornamental birds.

While the domesticated mallard evolved into this bewildering variety of shapes and sizes, the muscovy did nothing of the kind. It simply became bigger, fatter and uglier, though various different colours (including white, and black and white) appeared. Today, a domestic muscovy is still just a 'muscovy'. Muscovies will hybridise readily with domestic mallard, though the resulting offspring are infertile. However, mulards do make good table birds, as they are quick to mature (ready for the table at seven weeks) and carry less fat than a Pekin.

DUCKS IN CAPTIVITY

Once the pastime of royalty and the landed gentry, keeping a collection of wildfowl is a hobby now available to anyone with a garden and a pond. Few other captive birds look as good, or behave as naturally, as wildfowl. Though captive ducks are usually pinioned to stop them escaping, this seldom seems

Balinese duckherd, marching the flock out to the rice paddies to feed

much of a handicap to birds that spend up to eight weeks a year flightless, anyway. Ducks fly for a number of reasons, of which the most important are finding food, and escaping from enemies. In captivity, where they are kept supplied with food, and protected from their enemies by fences, being unable to fly is not much of a handicap.

Almost all the ducks have been kept in captivity at one time or another, and the great majority are firmly established in collections in

Europe and North America. Many are now several generations removed from their wild ancestors. Certain ducks are much better suited to captivity than others. Almost all the surface-feeding ducks do well in waterfowl collections, and so, too, do most of the freshwater diving ducks like the pochards. The sea ducks – scoters, eiders and mergansers – are rather more difficult, as they require special diets, and thrive only on ponds or lakes with adequate supplies of fresh, clear water. The most difficult species to keep are the ducks that like fast-flowing water, so few collections keep harlequins or torrent ducks, for example. Perhaps the rarest duck of all in waterfowl collections is the New Zealand blue duck, but the Wildfowl and Wetlands Trust has bred this species successfully for some years at Arundel.

The secret of success in keeping, and breeding, waterfowl in captivity is to create the ideal habitat for the birds in the collection. Most surface-feeding ducks will thrive with just a small, shallow pond, but they do need plenty of foraging area around the pond, with lots of natural cover for nesting. Diving ducks need deeper water – preferably at least a metre (3 feet) deep. Though ducks are naturally gregarious, they should never be kept in crowded conditions, as their pond will become fouled, the banks eroded, the natural vegetation around the pond destroyed. Over-crowding will also result in fights between rival drakes, and breeding success is certain to be poor.

In Britain there are several professional breeders of wildfowl, as well as many people who keep collections and sell the surplus stock they rear. Any-one interested in starting a wildfowl collection should seek the advice of a professional breeder, or an experienced duck keeper. The latter will be able to recommend the best species to start a collection with, and how best to protect the pond and its surroundings from predators. Ducks are invariably sold in pairs, and prices are surprisingly modest. A pair of mandarin or wigeon costs around £40, rising to about £150 for eiders.

Foxes are the main threat to captive ducks: there are a number of ways of keeping foxes out, of which the most usual is a fence at least 2 metres (6 feet) high, with an overhang at the top, and at least 15 centimetres (6 inches) buried underground to stop the foxes digging under. Fences such as this look unsightly in a garden, so the alternative is to use electric wires. Two live electric wires, one 15 centimetres (6 inches) above the ground, the second .6

WHEN ARE YOU GOING TO LEARN?

DANGER
ELECTRIC FENCE

metre (2 feet) high, backed by a 1 metre (3 feet) chicken-wire fence, can be remarkably effective. A friend with a large collection of wildfowl has used such a system for more than 10 years with no losses to foxes, despite an abundance of foxes (and badgers) around his house. Once a fox has touched the electric wire, it will never come near it again.

However, electric wires are not a deterrent to mink or rats, both of which can be a major problem to wildfowl keepers. Mink follow watercourses, and are proficient killers of waterfowl. The best way to protect duck from mink is to always keep cage traps along the edge of the fence. Mink are relatively easy to trap, but it is essential to always be prepared, even if no mink have been seen for a year or more. Rats are likely to be attracted to the surplus grain not eaten by the ducks, but as they will readily kill ducklings, and even attack adult teal, they should be killed (by trapping or poisoning) as soon as they appear.

Feeding captive wildfowl is simple: a mixture of wheat and chicken pellets will keep most species happy, but this should be supplemented as often as possible with any available greenery and vegetable matter. Lettuce and cabbage leaves, potatoes, even fresh lawn mowings, will all be eaten eagerly, while some ducks (such as mallard and mandarins) enjoy acorns and even sweet chestnuts. Sea ducks require special high-protein diets. Eiders, for example, are extremely greedy, and will stuff themselves on dog biscuits.

A measure of a collection's success is how many ducklings are reared each year. Captive ducks can be encouraged to nest by providing them with nest boxes or suitable nest sites. Shelduck will readily use a nest box buried in the ground, while mandarins prefer their nest boxes to be in a tree, with a ramp provided for access. Most ducks will nest in long grass, or under shrubs, so this sort of cover is essential for nesting. Sadly, few captive ducks make good parents (the most notable exceptions are the whistling ducks), so most waterfowl breeders take the eggs, and incubate them by putting them in an incubator, or under a broody bantam. The latter system is still favoured by many breeders, especially with rare or delicate ducks.

Under the Wildlife and Countryside Act, it is now an offence to keep most species of non-native ducks full-winged in collections, so the ducklings should be pinioned soon after they hatch. This is done by removing the bone at the end of one wing (with nail scissors), so that the primary feathers on that side never grow. Having a few full-winged birds in a collection does add to its attraction, and many people keep a few pairs of free-flying mandarins, or even pintail or wigeon. It is remarkable how some captive-bred ducks seldom stray away, even if left full-winged.

For many rare species of ducks, captive-breeding can be an important way of ensuring the birds' survival. There are certainly far more Laysan teal in collections than on Laysan island. The beautiful Carolina wood duck was nearly exterminated from its range in the eastern states of North America in the early years of the 20th century. Ironically, captive birds from Belgium and Holland were reimported to Connecticut, and over 9,000 of their offspring released in a successful attempt to re-establish this duck. Captive breeding and release programmes are also continuing with the brown teal in New Zealand, and the white-winged wood duck in Assam and Thailand.

Anyone contemplating starting a collection of waterfowl should join the British Waterfowl Association (secretary Mrs Ros Taylor, Gill Cottage, New Gill, Bishopdale, Leyburn, North Yorkshire DL8 3TQ). The BWA produces an excellent quarterly magazine, *Waterfowl*, as well the annual *Waterfowl Yearbook* and *Breeders' Directory*. The BWA caters for people who keep both wildfowl and domestic waterfowl.

Ducking

WILDFOWLING

Man has hunted wildfowl for hundreds of thousands of years, but it is only in the last century that wildfowling has become a sport rather than a job. It is an enormously popular sport, too, as in Europe and North America millions of sportsmen venture out each autumn and winter in pursuit of ducks. Quite how many ducks the fowlers manage to shoot remains a matter for guesswork, but in Britain an estimated 874,000 ducks are shot (and retrieved) annually. In addition, a significant proportion (perhaps as high as 30%) are shot but not found, or fly off wounded, to die miles from where they were shot at. Mallard are by far the most important quarry species in Britain, making up the bulk of the bag. However, teal and wigeon are also shot in significant numbers. Estimates suggest that the teal bag is around 150,000, and for wigeon anything between 50-100,000.

Remarkably, our wintering duck populations seem to be able to withstand such high mortality, and in recent years numbers of all the main quarry species have been rising, rather than declining. It is also important to point out that a considerable proportion of the mallard killed by sportsmen are birds that have been reared and released for shooting. As many as half a million mallard are released for shooting every year.

Shooting tame mallard is not regarded as real sport by the genuine wildfowler, who seeks his quarry on the saltings and mudflats, often under extremely difficult conditions. Few wildfowlers ever make large bags: many outings will be blank, while to go home with five or six ducks in the bag is generally regarded as exceptionally good. Though in Britain the duck shooting season starts on September 1st, serious coastal fowling does not get under way until November, and the best bags are usually made when the weather is at its wildest. Gale-force winds and rain force the birds to fly lower, so they are more likely to come in range of the waiting guns. The season finishes on January 31st, though there is an extension on the foreshore (below high-water mark) until February 20th.

Coastal wildfowling has a romantic image, and one enhanced by the writing of such authors as Peter Hawker, Sir Ralph Payne-Gallwey and Sir Peter Scott. Anyone who wants to try and understand the fascination and excitement of wildfowling should read Peter Scott's two beautifully illustrated classics, *Morning Flight* and *Wild Chorus*. I have done sufficient wildfowling to understand the draw it has on many people, but after my last outing on

the Medway estuary some years ago, I decided I would much rather watch ducks than try and shoot them. On this occasion I fell over in the thick, smelly mud, and got so cold I could hardly talk. Buying an oven-ready duck from the supermarket is a much easier and cheaper alternative if you want to eat duck for dinner.

Whatever one's moral views on wildfowling, it has to be acknowledged that wildfowlers are an important force when it comes to the conservation of duck habitats. In Britain, the British Association for Shooting and Conservation plays an active role in wildfowl research and conservation. Wildfowling is permitted on many National Nature Reserves, and the reserve's manager and the local wildfowling club usually have a close working relationship. A classic example is on the Ribble Estuary in Lancashire. This marsh was declared a NNR in 1979, when 5,000 wigeon wintered there. By the winter of 1994/95, wigeon numbers topped 110,000, a reflection of the  co-operation between English Nature and the Lytham and District Wildfowlers. The latter have their own marsh management team, have always had their own self-imposed sanctuary area for wildfowl, and also manage the cattle graziers on the marsh. During the shooting season they have very strict rules about shooting days and non-shooting days, while they also police the marsh against poachers. In 1989, the Lytham Wildfowlers purchased 400 acres of saltmarsh on the Ribble, and this land has been incorporated into the NNR.

The purchase of the saltings was partly funded by the BASC's Wildlife Habitat Trust, which was set up in 1986 as 'the UK hunters' conservation fund, dedicated to the acquisition, creation and management of wildlife habitats for the joint benefit of conservation and shooting'. Much of its funding comes from the UK Habitat Stamp. The Stamp was started in 1991, following the long-running and highly successful Duck Stamp run in the USA by the BASC's American counterpart, Ducks Unlimited. The Habitat Stamp (a stamp portraying either a duck or a goose, and painted by a leading wildlife artist) costs £5, with the profits going direct to the WHT. By 1995, sales of the stamps had raised £150,000.

In the USA, the duck stamp has been running since the 1930s, and has raised millions of dollars for the purchase of marshes, mainly on the duck breeding grounds in Canada. Duck stamps are bought by collectors, while duck hunters have to buy a stamp before going out shooting. Competition to paint the duck stamp is intense, and many North American wildlife artists launched their careers following success with their duck-stamp design.

OUTLAWING LEAD

Wildfowlers shoot ducks using shotguns. A shotgun cartridge contains around 300 pellets, and these spread out after the gun has been fired, giving a broad 'pattern'. Shooting a flying duck with a rifle, which fires just a single bullet, is all but impossible. Until recently, all shotgun pellets were made from lead, which was not only cheap to manufacture, but also had the ability to kill a duck cleanly at up to 36 metres (40 yards). However, spent lead pellets are frequently picked up by foraging wildfowl, and if the duck ingests sufficient pellets, it is likely to be killed by lead poisoning. In Britain, where most wildfowling takes place on coastal marshes with soft, gooey mud in which the pellets soon sink, lead poisoning has not been a major problem. However, lead pellets are now being phased for coastal fowling in a bid to reduce this risk to wildfowl. Lead pellets were outlawed in the USA, and a number of European countries, some time ago. There has, however, been lots of resistance to the switch from lead to steel, as the latter is harder, and thus prone to damage gun barrels. There is also still some doubt as to how effective it is, as many people fear that a greater number of ducks will be wounded (rather than killed) with steel than was the case with lead.

TOO MUCH LEAD

RINGING

It is by ringing, or what the Americans call 'banding', that we have managed to learn so much about where ducks travel to during their lives, and how long they can expect to live. The pioneer bird ringer was a Dane, H.C.C. Mortensen; in 1898 he ringed his first duck, a red-breasted merganser. It was recaptured soon afterwards, and this encouraged him to start a programme of duck ringing. He next turned his attention to teal, and from the first hundred he ringed, he had one recovery from the Netherlands, and no fewer than six from France. ('Recovery' is a ringing term for finding the bird, and its ring, again. Some recoveries are of trapped birds, others of individuals found dead. With ducks, the great majority of recoveries come from shooting.)

Since those early beginnings, hundreds of thousands of ducks have been ringed. A

Fixing the ring with pliers

considerable proportion have been recovered, as ducks are a popular sporting quarry, and most wildfowlers like to discover the origin of the duck they have shot.

Catching ducks for ringing is by no means easy. One of the most successful methods is using an old-fashioned duck decoy, where the ducks are lured into the trapping pipe by the decoyman's dog (see picture on p.105). The most effective decoy dogs are those that look like foxes. Ducks are curious birds, and will follow a fox in order to keep it in sight. If the fox-like decoy dog trots up the trapping pipe, many ducks will follow it. Once the ducks are well inside the pipe, the decoyman appears at the pipe entrance and scares the ducks into the trapping area.

Many other techniques have been used, from rocket netting (firing a net, with the aid of rockets, over a flock of feeding or resting birds), to catching ducklings with a fishing net. Currently the most popular method is the large cage trap, heavily baited with grain. All these methods work well with ducks that winter on freshwater, but very few sea ducks have been captured and ringed, so we know proportionately less about their movements.

Once captured, the duck has a lightweight alloy ring placed round its leg; this carries a number, and an address for the finder to send the ring to. The rings are designed to last the life of the duck. Though ringing can reveal a great deal, the technique does have its drawbacks and disadvantages. Most of the recoveries are of birds that have been shot, so the date of recovery

tends to reflect the seasons when duck shooting is allowed, giving a seasonal bias.

Some of the most interesting recoveries of ringed birds are off-course vagrants. For years no-one knew for certain whether genuine wild blue-winged teal crossed the Atlantic. Blue-winged teal are popular in captivity, so the birds that appeared here might have been escapees. Conclusive proof of

WATCHING FOR A KING

All the eiders are highly gregarious, so a lost or wandering individual of one species is sure to be attracted by a gathering of another. By carefully checking through the common eider flocks off the north or west coast of Scotland, you might just find a king eider, or, if you are really lucky, a Steller's eider. All the eiders are long-lived, and thus slow to mature. This means that the drakes may take up to four years to gain full maturity, and until they do so their plumage may be highly confusing. With practice all the eiders can be separated from each other by their different head shapes and bill structures, but trying to pick out a female king eider mixed in with a group of common eiders can be the ultimate test of one's ornithological ability. This is especially true if the birds are bobbing about on a rough sea half a mile offshore. Records of female king eiders in British waters are few, but if they occur as often as the drakes, then many must be overlooked.

cross-Atlantic passage came when a bird ringed in New Brunswick was re-covered in Suffolk in September 1971. The year before, a blue-wing from Prince Edward Island was found in Morocco, and another Prince Edward bird turned up in Spain's Ebro Delta in 1974. American wigeon ringed in New Brunswick have also been shot in Britain. A duckling ringed there on August 6th, 1966, was shot two months later in Shetland. That European ducks cross the other way is shown by a teal, ringed in England in Novem-ber, which was shot in Newfoundland four weeks later. Quite what route these ducks took to cross the Atlantic will always remain a mystery.

DUCK WATCHING

Few birds are more relaxing to watch than ducks. The combination of their attractive shapes, colours and noises gives them a special appeal. Duck watch-ing is a hobby open to almost anyone, as most town parks support a thriving population of mallard, and often a supporting cast of pochard and tufted ducks. Such urban ducks are usually both tame and approachable, and easy to study without even using binoculars. When I worked in London, I fre-quently escaped to St James's Park to watch the ducks. Like all the Royal Parks, St James's has a fine collection of ornamental wildfowl, but it also attracts considerable numbers of genuine *wild*fowl. Ringing has shown that

most of the tufted ducks that winter in St James's Park are immigrants from Scandinavia and eastern Europe. However, at least 30 pairs of tufted ducks attempt to nest in the Park every year. Unusual ducks can even turn up, and a long-tailed duck has been recorded on St James's Park lake. However, with so many pinioned birds present it can be difficult to know what is wild and what is tame.

For the duckwatcher who ventures out of town, good binoculars are essential. Duck watching in winter can often be a wet business, so binoculars that are totally waterproof are a good investment. I use either Leica 8x32 or Swarvoski 8x30: magnifications of more than 10x are difficult to hold steady, and 8x is the best compromise. A telescope, mounted on a sturdy tripod, is also invaluable for duck watching. Avoid using scopes with zoom eyepieces: the best scopes from manufacturers such Leica, Swarovski, Kowa and Nikon work best with a 30x wide-angle eye piece.

In Britain there is no problem finding somewhere to watch ducks, as almost all our wetland reserves are good, especially in the winter. The Wildfowl and Wetlands Trust refuges all offer superb viewing, invariably from comfortable hides. The WWT captive collections are also well worth visiting. Slimbridge has the most complete collection, but my favourite is Arundel, where spring-water from the chalk provides ideal conditions for displaying the birds to their best advantage. Many private duck collections are also open to the public. The best is Pensthorpe, in North Norfolk, with a remarkably comprehensive collection of birds, all kept in top condition.

Duck watching can be addictive, and I have now travelled around much of the world in pursuit of wildfowl. Many ducks are easy to see if you get to the right place, but getting there can be a problem! It is also frustrating to visit distant areas and miss the bird you really wanted to see. Bronze-winged ducks eluded me in Patagonia, and freckled ducks in Western Australia. I have seen all the ducks on the African list bar one: Hartlaub's. To see this elusive species I will have to make an expedition to the rainforests of Zaire or the Congo. In Europe, only Steller's eider eludes me, while the only North American duck I have yet to see in the wild is the spectacled eider. There are still quite enough ducks missing from my list to keep me busy looking for them for many years yet. However, though the lure of seeing new ducks is considerable, I still get a tremendous thrill from seeing old friends. What can beat a courting party of teal on a bright autumn day, or a flight of pintail against a sunset? My favourite quote (and the words used on the screensaver of my computer) comes from F.W. Harvey's *Ducks*: 'From the troubles of the world I turn to ducks.' If only more people did so, then the world would be a better place.

PHOTOGRAPHY
Few birds make more delightful subjects for the camera than ducks, while duck photography has introduced many people to the delights, and challenges, of wildlife photography. Photographing tame ducks in wildfowl collections, or even public parks, is as good a place to start as anywhere. Though it is possible to take interesting photographs with a compact

camera, you really need a single-lens-reflex camera with a telephoto lens, preferably with a motordrive or automatic film wind-on. The latter allows you to take a series of photographs without having to take your eye away from the viewfinder. Telephoto lenses do not have to be very long, and at places like the Wildfowl and Wetlands Trust reserves at Slimbridge, Martin Mere and Arundel, and even St James's Park in London, you will be able to get close enough to the birds to take satisfactory pictures with a 135mm lens. I started my duck photography with a 135mm lens, and managed to get a number of my photographs published. However, for more serious photography a lens of at least 300mm is better, while I now use a 400mm lens for most of my work.

One of the attractions of photographing ducks at the Wildfowl and Wetlands Trust reserves is the number of genuine wild birds that fly in to join the pinioned collection. Many of these wild birds become tame and approachable when in the collection, and thus ideal for photography.

There are a few secrets to taking successful duck photographs. For a start, if you want to take sharp pictures, always use a tripod with telephoto lenses longer than 200mm. With fast film it is possible to get away with hand-holding a long lens, but by using the tripod you will have a much higher success rate. With transparencies, most serious photographers prefer to use slow, finely grained film, usually 64 or 100asa. The slower the film the slower the shutter speed, so seldom will you be able to use a faster speed than 250th of a second. This is often too slow to stop movement, especially if a duck is bathing or flapping its wings. However, if you use a faster film (such as 400asa), you will also be able to use faster shutter speeds, and thus freeze any movement. Most 400asa print films are of high quality, and well worth using for duck photography.

Ducks invariably look their best when the sun is shining, so photography on dull days is seldom as satisfactory. A low angle from the sun often illuminates

ducks in an interesting way, so taking pictures in the morning or afternoon is usually more effective than in the middle of the day. Normally it is best to have the sun behind you when you take a photograph, but back-lighting (shooting into the sun) can produce interesting effects.

When taking portraits of ducks, try and ensure that there is a highlight in the duck's eye when you press the shutter – it is surprising how much difference that speck of light makes to the final result. If you are photographing pinioned ducks in a collection, try and take your photograph from the non-pinioned side, a rule many photographers overlook. (Take a look at the duck photographs in a photographic field guide. It is often possible to spot the tame ducks simply because the photographer has ignored this simple rule.) Photographing tame ducks with a long telephoto lens will often give the impression that the birds were wild. Long lenses have a narrow depth of field, so if you photograph a duck at 18 metres (60 feet) with a 400mm lens, using a wide aperture (such as f5.6), only the duck will be in focus.

For pictures with impact, get as low as possible to your subject. Photographs of ducks swimming on water, taken from above, are invariably dull to look at. The same birds, photographed at their own level, will look far more interesting. Do not be afraid to experiment – film is the cheapest part of photography.

Photographing flying ducks is a considerable challenge, and you will have to expect a fairly low success rate. When taking flying pictures, it is essential to swing the camera with the ducks, and keep it moving as you press the shutter. In this way the ducks should be sharp, even if the background is blurred.

Trying to take photographs of wild ducks away from reserves or collections can be very difficult, as the birds are generally wary and unapproachable. Using a car as a mobile hide can be effective, and often the only way to get close. Some wild ducks are much more approachable than others. In the Falklands, for example, I found the steamer ducks to be ridiculously tame and approachable, and the crested ducks and speckled teal were also very co-operative. However, the silver teal and yellow-billed pintail I encountered never let me approach close enough to have their pictures taken. Where ducks are used to seeing people your chances of getting good photographs are much higher. I once had tremendous fun photographing plumed and wandering whistling ducks from a boat in Kakadu National Park, in Northern Territory, Australia. The water was calm, my boat flat-bottomed, so I was able to set my camera up on a tripod. The boatman was skilled in getting the boat close to the birds, so I got lots of good photographs.

Though most species of ducks have been photographed extensively, particularly in captivity, there are still a good number of species that have rarely been portrayed in the wild. For the adventurous photographer, there are plenty of challenges available. How about going to New Guinea to photograph Salvadori's teal, or trying to capture on film Hartlaub's duck on the forest pools of West Africa? However, some of my best shots are of the humble mallard, a duck available to any British photographer.

MEMORABLE MERGANSERS

The strikingly patterned drake hooded merganser, with his erectile crest, is arguably the most handsome of all the sawbills. It is a forest bird, usually found on secluded streams and ponds surrounded by trees. This can make this species frustratingly difficult to watch in the wild, as the birds tend to draw back into the undergrowth when they think they are being watched. I have seen hooded mergansers several times in the USA, but most memorable were the birds I watched at Catahoula National Wildlife Refuge, Louisiana, in January 1982. Exceptionally cold weather had iced the Spanish moss on the trees surrounding the lake, which was also partially frozen. The little group of hooded mergansers were brilliantly illuminated by the low winter sun, producing an unforgettable picture.

Books
a duckperson's library

There is one book that every duck enthusiast's library should include: *Wildfowl, An identification guide to the ducks, geese and swans of the world* (Helm/A.& C. Black). Written by Steve Madge, and with 47 superb colour plates by Hilary Burn, it is the wildfowl book I refer to most often. Over 700 birds are depicted on the plates, showing each species in almost every plumage you are likely to encounter. Apart from notes on field identification, voice and a description of the plumage, the text also includes details of habits and behaviour. *Wildfowl* is the natural descendant of Peter Scott's *A Coloured Key to the Wildfowl of the World*, which was originally published in black and white in 1950, and made its first appearance in colour in 1957. It depicts all 247 forms of the 151 species of ducks, geese and swans recognised at the time of publication.

Few people have ever painted wildfowl better than Peter Scott, and his illustrations appear in many books. Some of his best work appeared in Jean Delacour's *The Waterfowl of the World*, published by Country Life in four volumes between 1954 and 1964. As a schoolboy duck enthusiast, I used to go the reference section of my local library every Saturday to consult *The Waterfowl of the World*. It still remains a valuable source of reference. Jean Delacour was the greatest French ornithologist of the 20th century, and one of my fondest memories is of having lunch with him at his château at Clères in Normandy in 1976. Delacour was then in his late '80s, but his brain was crystal sharp, and he was still a marvellous story teller.

None of my waterfowl books have better photographs than *Waterfowl, Ducks, Geese & Swans of the World*, by Frank S. Todd (Seaworld Press, 1979). Apart from its rather clumsy shape, this is a magnificent book, profusely illustrated with a tremendous collection of colour photographs depicting virtually every species in a variety of postures and plumages.

For anyone interested in the courtship display of wildfowl, then Paul A. Johnsgard's *Handbook of Waterfowl Behaviour* is a must. It was first published by Cornell University Press in 1965, but it remains the classic work on the subject.

Dr Jeffrey Harrison was a rarity, a man who was equally respected as a wildfowler, conservationist and ornithologist. His book, *A Wealth of Wildfowl*, was published by Andre Deutsch in 1967, and later appeared in paperback. Although now dated, it still makes a good read. Jeffrey Harrison also contributed to a number of other wildfowl books, including *The New*

Wildfowler in the 1970s, which remains the standard handbook for wildfowlers.

For students of wildfowl distribution in Britain the best reference remains *Wildfowl in Great Britain*, by Myrfyn Owen, G.L. Atkinson-Willes and D.G. Salmon. The first edition was published by HMSO in 1963, the second by the Wildfowl Trust and Nature Conservancy Council in 1986. The North American equivalent is *Ducks Geese and Swans of North America*, by Frank C. Bellrose, which has gone through a number of editions. It is published by Stakpole Books.

Most of the standard field guides do a reasonable job on ducks, but there is no doubt that Swedish artist Lars Jonsson paints them as well as anyone. His field guide, *The Birds of Europe* (Helm/A.&C. Black), is strongly recommended for this reason. Of the major reference works, the *Handbook of the Birds of the World* Volume I (Lynx, 1993) is noteworthy for its beautifully painted colour plates, and the outstanding photographs which illustrate the wildfowl chapters.

One of the most accomplished duck artists is Trevor Boyer, and his paintings in *Ducks of Britain and the Northern Hemisphere* (Dragon's World, 1986) are simply superb. The text is by John Gooders. For those who want to learn about duck distribution in Britain, then by far the best books to turn to are *The Atlas of Wintering Birds in Britain and Ireland* and *The New Atlas of Breeding Birds in Britain and Ireland: 1987-1991*. Both are published by T.&A.D. Poyser in association with the British Trust for Ornithology, and include fine maps accompanied by a highly informative text.

For my 12th birthday my sister gave me *A Paddling of Ducks*, by Dillon Ripley (Arthur Baker, 1959). It is a very enjoyable read, and inspired me to start my own collection of waterfowl. There are a number of books on keeping ducks in captivity, but one of the best remains *Ornamental Waterfowl*, by W.H. Payn and A.A. Johnson (Spur Publications, 1979).

Surprisingly few books describe the thrill of finding and watching ducks, but anyone with an interest in wildfowl will enjoy reading the three volumes of Peter Scott's *Travel Diaries of a Naturalist* published by Collins. His account of the 'Blue Duck Expedition' in Volume I is a classic. Peter Scott once told me that he had seen all the world's wildfowl in the wild, with the exception of the Chinese merganser, which he might have seen, but never got close enough to be sure.

Janet Kear worked with Peter Scott for many years at the Wildfowl Trust, and she is the author of another notable book, *Man and Wildfowl* (T.& A.D. Poyser, 1990). As its title suggests, it covers the relationships between birds and man, but it is exceptionally readable, and full of fascinating facts. For an understanding of duck relationships and taxonomy,

Evolution Illustrated by Waterfowl, by David Lack (published by Blackwell in association with the Wildfowl Trust, 1974) is unrivalled, and discusses such subjects as the ducks of remote islands, sexual selection and convergent evolution in an interesting and easily understandable way. Opinions on duck taxonomy have changed since its publication, but it remains a valuable work of reference.

Though the majority of the books I have mentioned here are out of print, they are all titles worth looking for in second-hand book shops, or to order from your library.

A checklist of the world's living ducks

(with their alternative names, and scientific names) This follows the order and taxonomy of Burt L.Monroe and Charles G. Sibley, as published in *A World Checklist of Birds* (1993). It is the simplest classification of the world's waterfowl, and recognises two species that in the past have been lumped with others: the Andean duck and the Sunda teal. The alternative names include a number of old country names, or names used by wildfowlers, many of which are rarely used today. The list of alternative names given is by no means exhaustive, and I have ignored several. For example, a surprising number of ducks have been called wigeon, or canvasback, other than the official holders of those names.

Only rarely do birdwatchers use such names incorrectly, but wildfowlers and duck hunters often do. If you meet an American duck hunter who tells you that he has shot a couple of blue-bills and a butterball, it is useful to know what he is talking about. However, it is important to note that the same slang name is often applied to different ducks; butterball, for example, may mean either bufflehead or ruddy duck.

In Britain, ornamental-duck enthusiasts use their own favoured names, such as Carolina for North American wood duck, Bahama pintail for white-cheeked pintail, and versicolour teal for silver teal. All the whistling ducks were once called tree ducks, and some modern books still use this out-dated term.

Family: DENDROCYGNIDAE

Spotted whistling duck	*Dendrocygnina guttata*
Plumed whistling duck (Eyton's whistling duck, grass whistle duck, grey or red-legged whistler)	*D. eytoni*
Wandering whistling duck (East Indian whistling duck, diving whistling duck, water whistle-duck)	*D. arcuata*
Black-billed whistling duck (Cuban whistling duck)	*D. arborea*
Fulvous whistling duck	*D. bicolor*
Lesser whistling duck (Javan whistling duck, Indian whistling duck)	*D. javanica*
White-faced whistling duck	*D. viduata*
Red-billed whistling duck (Black-bellied whistling duck)	*D. autumnalis*

Family ANATIDAE
Subfamily Oxyurinae

Masked duck	*Oxyura dominica*
Ruddy duck (Butterball, bull-necked teal)	*O. jamaicensis*
Andean duck (Peruvian ruddy duck)	*O. ferruginea*
White-headed duck	*O. leucocephala*
Maccoa duck	*O. maccoa*
Argentine blue-bill (Lake duck, Argentine ruddy duck)	*O. vittata*
Blue-billed duck (Australian blue-bill, spinetail, little musk duck)	*O. australis*
Musk duck (Mould goose, steamer)	*B. lobata*
Blackheaded duck	*Heteronetta atricapilla*

Subfamily Stictonettinea

Freckled duck (Oatmeal duck, speckled duck)	*Stictonetta naevosa*

Subfamily Anatinae
Tribe Anserini

Common shelduck (Sheldrake, burrow duck)	*Tadorna tadorna*
Ruddy shelduck (Brahminy duck)	*T. ferruginea*
Cape shelduck (South African shelduck)	*T. cana*
Australian shelduck (Chestnut-breasted shelduck, mountain duck, grunter, chestnut sheldrake)	*T. tadornoides*
Paradise shelduck (New Zealand shelduck, painted duck)	*T. variegata*
Crested shelduck (Korean shelduck)	*T. cristata*
Radjah shelduck (Burdekin duck, white-headed shelduck)	*T. radjah*
Flightless steamerduck	*Tachyeres pteneres*
Chubut steamerduck	*T. leucocephalus*
Falkland steamerduck (Loggerhead, logger)	*T. brachypterus*
Flying steamerduck (Canvasback)	*T. patachonicus*
Muscovy duck	*Cairina moschata*
White-winged duck (White-winged wood duck)	*Cairina scutulata*
Hartlaub's duck	*Pteronetta hartlaubi*
Comb duck (Kob-billed duck/goose, nukta)	*Sarkidiornis melanotos*
Green pygmy goose (Green dwarf goose, goose-teal)	*Nettapus pulchellus*
Cotton pygmy goose (Cotton teal, white pygmy goose, white-quilled pygmy goose)	*N. coromandelianus*
African pygmy goose	*N. auritus*

Tribe Anatini

Ringed teal	*Callonetta leucophrys*
Carolina wood duck (North American wood duck, summer duck, woodie, acorn duck)	*Aix sponsa*
Mandarin duck	*A. galericulata*
Maned duck (Australian wood duck, maned goose)	*Chenonetta jubata*
Brazilian teal (Brazilian duck)	*Amazonetta brasiliensis*
Torrent duck	*Merganetta armata*
Blue duck	*Hymenolaimus malacorhynchus*
Salvadori's teal	*Salvadorina waigiuensis*
Crested duck	*Anas speculariodes*
Bronze-winged duck (Spectacled duck)	*Anas specularis*
Cape teal (Cape wigeon)	*A. capensis*
Gadwall (Grey duck)	*A. strepera*
Falcated duck (Falcated teal)	*A. falcata*
Eurasian wigeon (European wigeon, widgeon)	*A. penelope*
American wigeon (Baldpate)	*A. americana*
Chiloe wigeon (Southern wigeon, black and white wigeon)	*A. sibilatrix*
African black duck	*A. sparsa*
American black duck (Black mallard, red leg)	*A. rubripes*
Mottled duck	*A. fulvigula*
Mallard (Wild duck, green-neck)	*A. platyrhynchos*
Hawaiian duck	*A. wyvilliana*
Laysan duck (Laysan teal)	*A. laysanensis*
Spot-billed duck (Spotbill)	*A. poecilorhyncha*
Philippine duck	*A. luzonica*
Pacific black duck (Brown, grey or wild duck)	*A. superciliosa*
Yellow-billed duck (Yellowbill)	*A. undulata*
Meller's duck	*A. melleri*
Blue-winged teal (Summer teal, bluewing)	*A. discors*
Cinnamon teal (Red teal)	*A. cyanoptera*
Cape shoveler	*A. smithii*
Red shoveler (Argentine shoveler)	*A. platalea*
Australian shoveler (Southern shoveler, New Zealand shoveler (shovelbill, stinker)	*A. rhynchotis*
Northern shoveler (Spoonbill, spoony)	*A. clypeata*
Madagascar teal (Bernier's teal)	*A. bernieri*
Grey teal (Slender or wood teal)	*A. gracilis*
Sunda teal (Andaman teal)	*A. gibberifrons*
Chestnut teal (Chestnut-breasted teal)	*A. castanea*
Brown teal (New Zealand teal, Aukland Islands teal, pateke)	*A. aucklandica*

White-cheeked pintail (Bahama pintail, Bahama duck, Galapagos pintail)	A. bahamensis
Red-billed teal (Red-billed pintail)	A. erythrorhyncha
Speckled teal (Yellow-billed teal, Chilean teal, sharp-winged teal, Andean teal)	A. flavirostris
Northern pintail (Sea pheasant, sprigtail)	A. acuta
Eaton's pintail (Southern pintail)	A. eatoni
Yellow-billed pintail (Brown pintail, Chilean pintail, South Georgian teal)	A. georgica
Garganey (Summer teal)	A. querquedula
Baikal teal (Formosa teal)	A. formosa
Green-winged teal (Common teal, teal)	A. crecca
Puna teal	A. puna
Silver teal (Versicolour teal, Pampa teal)	A. versicolor
Hottentot teal	A. hottentota
Pink-eared duck (Zebra duck, pink-eyed duck, wigeon)	Malacorhynchus membranaceus
Marbled teal (Marbled duck)	Marmaronetta angustirostris
Red-crested pochard	Netta rufina
Rosy-billed pochard (Rosybill)	N. peposaca
Southern pochard (Red-eyed pochard)	Aythya erythrophthalma
Common pochard (European pochard)	A. ferina
Canvasback	A. valisineria
Redhead (Pochard)	A. americana
Ring-necked duck (Ring-bill)	A. collaris
Feruginous duck (White-eye, white-eyed pochard)	A. nyroca
Madagascar pochard (Madagascan white-eye)	A. innotata
Baer's pochard	A. baeri
Hardhead (White-eyed duck, copperhead, white-wing)	A. australis
Tufted duck (Tufted pochard, magpie diver)	A. fuligula
New Zealand scaup (Black teal)	A. novaeseelandiae
Greater scaup	A. marila
Lesser scaup (Bluebill)	A. affinis
Common eider (St Cuthbert's duck, coo-doos, great black-and-white duck)	Somateria mollissima
King eider	S. spectabilis
Spectacled eider (Fischer's eider)	S. fischeri
Steller's eider	P. stelleri
Harlequin duck	Histionicus histrionicus
Long-tailed duck (Old squaw, sea pintail)	Clangula hyemalis
Black scoter (Common scoter)	Melanitta negra
Velvet scoter (White-winged scoter)	M. fusca

Surf scoter	*M. perspicillata*
Common goldeneye (Whistler)	*Bucephala clangula*
Barrow's goldeneye (Rocky mountain whistler)	*B. islandica*
Bufflehead (Butterball, dipper)	*B. albeola*
Smew (White nun)	*Mergellus albellus*
Hooded merganser	*Lophodytes cucullatus*
Brazillian merganser	*Mergus octosetaceus*
Red-breasted merganser (Sawbill, fish duck)	*M. serrator*
Scaly-sided merganser (Chinese merganser, scaly merganser)	*M. squamatus*
Goosander (Common merganser)	*M. merganser*

Index

Page numbers in bold indicate illustrations

If you have enjoyed this book, you might be interested in other natural history titles we publish; write for a free booklist to 18 Anley Road, London W14 OBY. You may purchase the titles below either from bookshops or direct from us. All are priced at £7.99 except where indicated, and all are illustrated with line drawings throughout. Please add £1.50 p & p when ordering direct:

World Wildlife Series

ANTS
Ray North

BIG CATS
Douglas Richardson
(£9.99)

CHIMPANZEES
Tess Lemmon

DOLPHINS
Peter Evans

PARROTS
David Alderton
(£9.99)

PENGUINS
John A. Love

SEA OTTERS
John A. Love
(£9.99)

SPIDERS
Michael Chinery

British Natural History Series

BADGERS
Michael Clark

BATS
Phil Richardson

DEER
Norma Chapman

EAGLES
John A. Love

FALCONS
Andrew Village

FROGS AND TOADS
Trevor Beebee

GARDEN CREEPY-CRAWLIES
Michael Chinery

HEDGEHOGS
Pat Morris

MAMMAL DETECTIVE
Rob Strachan

MICE AND VOLES
John Flowerdew

OTTERS
Paul Chanin

OWLS
Chris Mead

POND LIFE
Trevor Beebee

PONIES IN THE WILD
Elaine Gill

PUFFINS
Kenny Taylor

RABBITS AND HARES
Anne McBride

ROBINS
Chris Mead

SEALS
Sheila Anderson

SNAKES AND LIZARDS
Tom Langton

SQUIRRELS
Jessica Holm

STOATS AND WEASELS
Paddy Sleeman

URBAN FOXES
Stephen Harris

URBAN WILDLIFE
Peter Shirley

WHALES
Peter Evans

WILDCATS
Mike Tomkies